What People Are Saying About Environmental Solutions

". . . [T]he banning of DDT was one of the most important legal victories ever won for wildlife."

>—*Russell E. Train*
>*Former Chairman*
>*World Wildlife Fund U.S.*

"Removing lead from gasoline alone may be preventing tens of thousands of cases of lead poisoning in children annually."

>—*Dr. Irving J. Selikoff*
>*Professor Emeritus of Environmental Medicine*
>*Mount Sinai School of Medicine*

". . . [L]eadership and scientific insight have saved our great Rocky Mountain parks from the major source of acid rain."

>—*Paul C. Pritchard*
>*President*
>*National Parks and Conservation Association*

What People Are Saying About EDF

"EDF embodies the practical notion that environmental problems need rational solutions . . . solutions that protect our world without hurting ourselves."

> —*John Chancellor*

"Few organizations have contributed so much fresh thinking about fresh water as EDF, in its ingenious master plans for water quality and conservation."

> —*Representative Morris K. Udall*
> *Chairman*
> *House Interior Committee*

"EDF is playing a critical role in promoting sustainable development in the multilateral banks and defending the Earth's stratospheric ozone. Future generations will be grateful for its efforts."

> —*Dr. Mostafa K. Tolba*
> *Executive Director*
> *United Nations Environment Programme*

EDF's 9 for the 90's

YOU can help address the 9 most critical environmental issues of the 1990's.

Nearly all of today's environmental problems stem from human activities of the past 100 years, with the worst damage only recently having been put on display.

In 1962, when Rachel Carson's *Silent Spring* first warned of serious harm, it was still not possible even to conceive of humankind's punching a hole through the ozone layer . . . or turning the rains acid . . . or tampering with the planetary thermostat. Yet we have done all these things, utterly unaware of our own strength.

Now, at last, people from all corners of the globe are awakening to environmental problems and demanding effective solutions. The next 9 pages show some of the steps EDF is taking toward those solutions, plus 9 personal steps YOU can take.

THE GREENHOUSE EFFECT

EDF Action for the 1990's:

Facilitate summit meetings between American and Soviet scientists and economists. Join in United Nations world climate conference.

Goal for the Year 2000:

An international agreement is reached to dramatically reduce gases responsible for the Greenhouse Effect and implementation has begun.

One Personal Step You Can Take:

Get your community to plant more trees or plant one yourself. Trees absorb carbon dioxide, the chief greenhouse gas.

WILDLIFE AND HABITAT

EDF Action for the 1990's:

Work to save endangered sea turtles and porpoises.
Push for more effective protection of endangered
species. Guarantee no net loss to U.S. wetlands.
Urge enforcement of the MARPOL treaty to end
ocean dumping of plastic trash.

Goal for the Year 2000:

Endangered species from around the world are
brought back from the brink of extinction. And our
oceans are made clean again.

One Personal Step You Can Take:

Snip plastic six-pack rings before discarding, to
prevent them from ever ensnaring wildlife.

OZONE DEPLETION

EDF Action for the 1990's:

Press for strengthing of the Montreal Accord to hasten the phaseout of ozone-depleting CFCs. Provoke state-level action to capture and recycle CFCs found in refrigerators and home and auto air conditioners.

Goal for the Year 2000:

Worldwide production of ozone-depleting CFCs ended.

One Personal Step You Can Take:

Urge your appliance repair service to use equipment that recycles CFCs when servicing refrigerators and home and auto air conditioners.

SAVING THE RAINFORESTS

EDF Action for the 1990's:

Push Brazil to designate additional rainforest reserves. Encourage preservation of forests in Indonesia and India. Continue to press development banks to invest in rainforest conservation.

Goal for the Year 2000:

Funding of destructive projects is ended. Rainforest reserves are greatly enlarged.

One Personal Step You Can Take:

Buy products such as Brazil nuts that can be harvested from the rainforests safely and perpetually.

ACID RAIN

EDF Action for the 1990's:

Work with Congress to pass a strong acid rain bill incorporating powerful market incentives.

Goal for the Year 2000:

Destructive acid rain is a thing of the past, thanks to strictly-enforced pollution cuts and a permanent cap on sulfur emissions.

One Personal Step You Can Take:

Conserve electricity to reduce the sulfur dioxide and greenhouse gases emitted from power plants.

ANTARCTICA

EDF Action for the 1990's:

Voice the concerns of Antarctica wildlife at international meetings on the Antarctica treaty. Push for stringent environmental safeguards to protect Antarctica from oil spills and other pollution.

Goal for the Year 2000:

This pristine continent is designated as a world park.

One Personal Step You Can Take:

Write U.S. and U.N. officials to support the establishment of Antarctica as a permanent preserve.

TOXICS

EDF Action for the 1990's:

Press for national toxics disclosure laws on the model of California's Proposition 65. Develop and advocate strong Federal toxics controls. Encourage source reduction to curb the creation of new toxic waste.

Goal for the Year 2000:

Existing toxic waste is cleaned up, and industrial practices are changed to prevent creation of new toxic waste.

One Personal Step You Can Take:

Choose products with few or no hazardous ingredients.

WATER

EDF Action for the 1990's:

Help establish state-level clean water standards. Build incentives to preserve water. Force investigation of groundwater quality near hazardous waste sites and leaking underground tanks.

Goal for the Year 2000:

Clean and abundant water is guaranteed for generations to come.

One Personal Step You Can Take:

Use only phosphate-free detergents. Try to avoid using pesticides on your lawn or garden.

RECYCLING

EDF Action for the 1990's:

Step up nationwide efforts to make curbside recycling widespread and convenient. Expand markets for recycled goods. Encourage businesses to use recyclable packaging. Educate communities about the cost-effectiveness and environmental safety of recycling instead of incineration and landfilling.

Goal for the Year 2000:

At least 50% of all trash is recycled across America.

One Personal Step You Can Take:

Donate reusable and repairable clothing and other items to charity instead of throwing them away. Participate in a local recycling program or join efforts to start one.

Ahead of the Curve

Shaping New Solutions
To Environmental Problems

Robert E. Taylor

Environmental Defense Fund
New York, NY
Washington, DC
Oakland, CA
Boulder, CO
Richmond, VA
Raleigh, NC
Austin, TX

EDF is a non-profit organization that relies on your support to continue its work to find lasting solutions to environmental problems. All gifts are tax deductible. For further information, please contact the national headquarters:

Environmental Defense Fund
257 Park Avenue South
New York, New York 10010
Telephone 212 505-2100

CONTENTS

5 Foreword

7 Prologue

11 The Birth of Environmentalism

23 Getting the Lead Out

33 The Tortoise and the Snare

39 Throwing It All Away

45 Only One Earth

53 Up in Smoke

65 The Gray Triangle: Acid Over the West

72 Clearing the Air

84 Power Struggle

98 Liquid Assets

109 Epilogue

FOREWORD

Environmental groups are as varied as businesses. Whether you want to protect brook trout or whales, your own lungs or the world's climate, there's an environmental group that pursues your goals. Among them you can find every approach from persuasion to injunction to revolution.

The Environmental Defense Fund attracted me for two reasons: it does top-notch scientific research and it puts the results to work. I've never seen EDF's people obstructing progress; I see them taking tough problems apart and putting solutions together.

I also admire people breaking new ground. Founded by scientists, EDF was the first major environmental group to use the courts to stop environmental harm. Later, it was among the first to hire full-time Ph.D. economists to help put market incentives on the side of the environment. Increasingly, EDF has turned to the financial carrot rather than the legal stick, though it keeps both at hand.

This book, written by veteran journalist Robert E. Taylor with the EDF staff, gives you a behind-the-scenes look at a few recent episodes in the environmental movement. I think they are convincing proof that individuals can make a difference in the environment, not only by filing lawsuits or chaining themselves to plant gates, but by showing the power of good science, sound economics and, most of all, creative ideas.

Lewis S. Ranieri
Member, EDF Board of Trustees

PROLOGUE

The East Room of the White House was already crowded. Elbowing into ranks of chairs was an unlikely collection of people: auto executives and union organizers, lawmakers and electric utility lobbyists, governors, oilmen, and environmental activists.

These were the troops of the annual Clean Air Act battles that had stymied congressional action for a decade. But now change was in the air. President Bush had called them together to unveil his bid to end the stalemate.

Striding to the front of the room, Bush proceeded to lay out an ambitious proposal that would cut nearly in half the electric power plant emissions that cause acid rain. It would offer companies a wide choice among pollution-reduction methods, giving each plant owner an incentive to choose the most efficient approach based on local economic conditions. Bush said harnessing such market incentives would be "the fastest, most cost-effective way" to clean the air.

At that, three men in the audience breathed more easily. The team from the Environmental Defense Fund had spent the past six months crafting and advocating an acid rain control proposal built around market incentives. Some officials had balked at the trio's unconventional ideas, but Bush's words made clear that EDF's advice had been taken; the market concept was now the foundation of a powerful plan to end acid rain.

Helping to break the Washington logjam on clean air may have tied up three EDF specialists for six months, but it left no shortage of expertise to be deployed elsewhere in the world. An EDF anthropologist returned from Brazil to meet with the president of the Inter-American Development Bank on provisions to protect the Amazon rainforest. An EDF scientist reached the remote U.S. Palmer Station in Antarctica, where he documented the effects of an Argentine oil spill that had blotted out years of research.

An EDF physicist flew to London as the only American environmentalist invited to brief Prime Minister Margaret Thatcher and her cabinet on global warming and the greenhouse effect. Three EDF colleagues departed for Moscow, where they would meet with top Soviet environmental officials. And all this still left most of the environmental defenders stationed on the home front, where EDF's work began nearly a quarter-century ago.

Since its founding in 1967, EDF has led the way toward a new level of sophistication in environmentalism. It has grown from a living-room-full of citizens concerned about DDT use on Long Island to a nationwide organization with seven offices, more than 30 scientists and economists (over half of whom hold Ph.D.'s), 18 lawyers, more than 150,000 members, and an annual budget exceeding $15 million.

The group was founded on an innovative idea, that a merger of science and law would create a powerful force for a better environment. That concept has paid huge dividends. While progress through court orders has slowed, EDF has continued to stay ahead of the curve, using new techniques to shape sensible alternatives to environmentally harmful practices.

"Environmentalists have to become architects of the future," says Fred Krupp, EDF's executive director. "There's a hunger for organizations that don't solely oppose problems, but themselves generate solutions. Instead of just saying 'No, you can't,' environmental groups ought to show how you can."

This book is a brief collection of stories that show some of what EDF has proposed. The group's role has not always been noticed. In the case of Bush's acid rain bill, however, the President himself paid an unusual tribute to EDF—and to the bipartisan project in which it joined—for their innovative way of looking at such problems.

"Let me commend Project 88 and groups like the Environmental Defense Fund," Bush said in unveiling his bill, "for bringing creative solutions to long-standing problems—for not only breaking the mold, but helping to build a new one."

THE BIRTH OF ENVIRONMENTALISM

"The forest and water problems are perhaps the
most vital internal questions of the United States."
President Theodore Roosevelt
First presidential message, 1901

"I am an environmentalist."
Vice President George Bush
Presidential campaign, 1988

When the original Earth Day bloomed full force in 1970,
it caught many Americans by surprise. With little warning, "teach-ins" filled thousands of schools and colleges
with talk about pollution, wildlife protection and parks.
A word barely heard a decade before, "environment"
was on the lips of the nation.

Today, almost everyone is an environmentalist. In
two decades, the movement's goals have permeated the
American psyche, worked their way into the nation's
laws, politics and economic system. Environmental protection has become institutionalized. Pollution abate-
ment and control provided 167,000 jobs in 1985. Every
major industrial company employs ranks of highly-
trained specialists on environmental compliance. The
business of environmental protection has become a
growth industry as many old problems persist and new,
global threats emerge.

Environmental groups have grown explosively too.
The National Wildlife Federation, the largest, has more
than five million supporters and a recent annual budget
of more than $60 million.

   Growth has promoted diversity. The environmentalist
label lately has been stretched all the way from patrician
Republican wildlife enthusiast Nathaniel Reed to the
roughneck Sea Shepherds, who rammed and scuttled a
vessel that was believed to be ignoring restrictions on
whaling; from protesters opposing neighborhood dumps
to Ph.D. scientists leading international conferences on
the greenhouse effect.

   While modern environmentalism in one sense dates
from Earth Day 1970, its roots go back a century and
more. Men like Henry David Thoreau, Walt Whitman
and George Perkins Marsh planted the intellectual seeds
in the mid-19th century. These sprouted near the end of
the century into the "conservation" movement in reaction
against land plundering in the robber-baron era. As ur-
banization spread, inspirational leaders like John Muir,
founder of the Sierra Club, helped graft protection of
wildlife and wilderness onto the conservation ethic. It
wasn't until the 1960's and 1970's that it bloomed into
pollution prevention and protection of human health.
Only then did the word "environmentalist" come into
widespread use.

   Gifford Pinchot, first director of the U.S. Forest Service, recorded the awakening of the movement in the
late 1800's in his memoir, *Breaking New Ground*. Public
lands in the West, he wrote, were being despoiled by
timber companies, railroads and miners. Placer mining
of gold, for example, ravaged California landscapes with
torrents of water, washing tons of earth into rivers for
each ounce of gold recovered. "At a time when, in the
West, the penalty for stealing a horse was death—death

without benefit of the law—stealing the public land in open defiance of the law was generally regarded with tolerance or even approval."

Then, toward the turn of the century, the federal government began setting aside occasional jewels of Western land into parks. Yellowstone National Park was established in 1872, eight years after California reserved the Yosemite Valley. Eventually the National Park Service was formed, though its domain grew only gradually, mostly through piecemeal acts of Congress.

Far larger tracts were taken up into what would become the national forests. In 1891—"without question and without debate," according to Pinchot—Congress authorized the president to reserve selected forest land against private ownership. The law freed presidents to take bold steps to conserve land for public uses. Benjamin Harrison reserved thirteen million acres. Grover Cleveland doubled that in the last ten days of his term. And Theodore Roosevelt, with characteristic vigor, jacked up the total to 194 million acres, created the Forest Service and put Pinchot at its helm.

Roosevelt used his bully pulpit to preach a new ethic called "conservation." In 1908, he hosted a week-long White House Conference on the subject. The star of the show was Pinchot, who had studied forestry in Europe. And the conservation ideal that he and Roosevelt preached wasn't preservation of pristine nature. It was optimal use: management of natural resources for the greatest good of the greatest number of people.

"Forest protection is not an end in itself," T.R. had proclaimed only a few months after taking office. "It is a means to increase and sustain the resources of our country and the industries which depend upon them. The preservation of our forests is an imperative business necessity."

In the late 19th century a competing ideal began to grow: that nature should be preserved for its own sake. The leading proponent was Pinchot's friend and one-time hiking companion John Muir, the avid outdoorsman who founded the Sierra Club.

The two ideals clashed memorably over a spectacular valley on California's Tuolumne River. Pinchot supported damming the river to provide water for the growing San Francisco area. Muir bitterly opposed it. Muir and his allies lost; the Hetch-Hetchy Valley became a reservoir for the greatest good.

Dam-building and forestry accelerated right through President Franklin Roosevelt's New Deal, but were abruptly shelved by World War II and left there during the postwar drive to feed, house, clothe and transport a booming U.S. population.

It wasn't until John F. Kennedy was elected president in 1960 that conservationist ideas surged again, by then intertwined with the preservationist philosophy of Muir. Kennedy and his Interior Secretary, Stewart L. Udall, voiced concern over the pollution and development of wilderness areas and proposed establishing a fund to finance further expansion of federal lands.

"Many nations no longer have the option of preserving part of their land in pristine condition," Udall wrote at the time in his book, *The Quiet Crisis*. "We must take ours up before it is too late. A wilderness system will offer man what many consider the supreme human experience."

———————

Rachel Carson's *Silent Spring*, published in 1962, was what first alerted the public to the broad destruction of wildlife being caused by highly toxic pesticides such as DDT. *Silent Spring* drove home a simple message: Man does not exist apart from nature around him, but is himself a part of it. In the poisoning of the natural world, an aroused public began to see the darker side of the postwar "miracles" of modern science. No longer could chemical pesticides masquerade as magic bullets supposedly homing in on unwanted species; just like real bullets, chemicals were now seen as fully capable of striking down innocent bystanders such as birds or fish or man.

Pesticide manufacturers quickly mounted an attempt to discredit *Silent Spring* and its author; President Kennedy set up a panel of his Science Advisory Committee to study the problem. The panel's report was described by Rachel Carson's biographer as "a complete vindication of her thesis," but it did not result in any immediate corrective action.

Then, in 1967, three scientists living on Long Island and a fourth in Michigan, who were as alarmed as Carson had been by the effects of DDT on wildlife, conceived of a new way to put these concerns into motion. They formed the Environmental Defense Fund, joined with an attorney, and became the first group to take scientific evidence into the courts to achieve

Early National
Conservation Organizations

Many of today's groups had their beginnings long before Rachel
Carson published *Silent Spring* in 1962.

	FOUNDED	RECENT MEMBERSHIP
American Forestry Association	1875	35,000
Sierra Club	1892	450,000
Wildlife Conservation International	1895	34,000
National Audubon Society	1905	550,000
National Parks and Conservation Association	1919	70,000
The Izaac Walton League of America	1922	50,000
The Wilderness Society	1935	220,000
National Wildlife Federation	1936	5,800,000
Ducks Unlimited	1937	610,000
Defenders of Wildlife	1947	80,000
The Nature Conservancy	1951	343,000
Friends of Animals	1957	120,000
Trout Unlimited	1959	58,000
World Wildlife Fund–U.S.	1961	500,000

Source: Conservation Directory

environmental goals. With support from the Ford Foundation through National Audubon's Rachel Carson Memorial Fund, EDF's founders brought case after case seeking to replace DDT with pest control methods less dangerous to wildlife. Before they were through, their efforts would lead to the nationwide banning of DDT and to the first established precedents of environmental law.

According to co-founder Dr. Charles Wurster, EDF "was born from the frustration of a group of environmentalists unable to move the system, to make it respond, to force environmental protection." And EDF's founders weren't alone in their frustration. A groundswell was building in response to Carson's writing, augmented by public revulsion at calamities such as the 1969 oil well blowout that blackened Santa Barbara's beaches.

The growing pressure erupted on Earth Day 1970. "A chorus of concern for the environment is sweeping the country," the President's Council on Environmental Quality wrote that year. "It reaches to the regional, national and international environmental problems. It embraces pollution of the earth's air and water, noise and waste and the threatened disappearance of whole species of plant and animal life."

Environmental groups grew and multiplied, and lobbying Washington became a major new activity. The Sierra Club lobbied so aggressively that, prodded by President Richard M. Nixon, the Internal Revenue Service stripped the group of its tax-exempt status.

Ironically, the move to curb pollution rose to full force during Nixon's presidency. It was Nixon who signed the National Environmental Policy Act, which required that major federal actions be studied for their possible environmental impacts. The Environmental Protection Agency was established. The Clean Air Act of 1970 and the Clean Water Act of 1972 were enacted.

The legislative gains continued into the 1980's, after Love Canal had helped turn the federal focus to the safe handling and disposal of toxic substances. President Ronald Reagan's Interior Secretary James Watt and EPA administrator Anne Gorsuch Burford largely failed to roll back environmental protections, but their efforts to do so made environmental group membership surge anew.

Litigation flourished. In the late 1960's and early 1970's, EDF's success fighting DDT helped spur a host of groups to arm themselves with attorneys. The Natural Resources Defense Council was launched with Ford Foundation funding. The Sierra Club spawned its Legal Defense Fund. The National Wildlife Federation and National Audubon Society started going to court. Environmentalists blocked dams, nuclear power plants and highway projects. They forced regulators to tighten pollution controls to meet ambitious statutory demands for clean air and rivers.

"The legal victories won in the late sixties and early seventies formed the foundation on which the modern environmental movement is built," declared NRDC executive director John Adams in *Crossroads: Environmental Priorities for the Future*. The same volume quotes David Sive, one of the first successful environmental litigators, saying: "In no other political or social movement has litigation played so important and dominant a role. Not even close."

But as time went on, many environmental lawyers

began to complain about diminishing returns. While courts could block actions, they often proved ill-suited to crafting solutions. And using courts in an attempt to steer government agencies could be clumsy and frustrating.

In 1986, for instance, EPA administrator William Ruckelshaus was threatened with a contempt of court citation and jail for refusing to set standards for radioactive emissions from uranium mines and some federal facilities. Ruckelshaus got the court off his back by pegging standards at existing emission levels. The lesson for one environmental lawyer was that you can force agencies to write rules, but you can't force them to write *good* rules.

Some observers also complained that environmental gains were diminishing—or disappearing—as government added new layers of legislation and new ranks of regulators.

By the mid-1980's some environmental group leaders started talking about new approaches that wouldn't rely on federal regulators, court orders or laws. A few prototypes were cited. In California, EDF had demonstrated that electric utilities didn't have to build massive new power plants to meet future demand. The Institute for Local Self-Reliance, a Washington, D.C., group, had shown Chester, Pennsylvania, how to develop and finance a trash recycling plant instead of an incinerator. The Sierra Club had helped a California timber company design a financial restructuring plan to ward off a corporate takeover.

In 1986, Fred Krupp, executive director of EDF, wrote in *The Wall Street Journal* about a third stage of the environmental movement. He suggested the environmental past could be seen in two stages. The first was the conservation era launched by T.R. and Pinchot. The second was the explosion of pollution control laws and regulations that followed *Silent Spring* and Earth Day 1970.

Krupp wrote that in the third stage, environmentalists should "recognize that behind the waste dumps and dams and power plants and pesticides that threaten major environmental harm, there are nearly always legitimate social needs—and that long-term solutions lie in finding alternative ways to meet those underlying needs. Otherwise, we are treating only symptoms; the problems will surface again and again. Answer the underlying needs, and you have a lasting cure."

As other environmentalists picked up on the theme, it became known as the Third Wave theory, after futurist Alvin Toffler's best seller. Different Third Wave concepts emerged, but the unifying theme was that the new wave should be solution-oriented. "We have won the struggle for acceptance with Main Street America, and now people are looking to us for solutions," said Lucy Blake, chairman of the League of Conservation Voters, in a 1986 interview with *The Los Angeles Times*. "It's not enough anymore to stand on the outside and take potshots."

Another fan of the Third Wave concept was later to become administrator of the EPA—William K. Reilly. As president of the Conservation Foundation, he led efforts to mediate between industry and environmental interests.

"Environmentalists have been enormously successful

at passing new laws," Reilly told the L.A. *Times* in 1986. "Yet real progress has been extraordinarily slow. What we've seen is endless litigation, and when the litigation is over everybody runs back to Congress to change the law. We concluded there must be a faster way to make progress."

Third Wavers draw their share of criticism. Some hard-line environmentalists have accused them of compromising their principles.

Dr. Barry Commoner, the noted environmental scientist and writer, has charged that big, national environmental groups are selling out. In *Crossroads,* he argued that in negotiating compromises, environmental groups may "become hostage to the corporations' power and will experience the Stockholm Syndrome, in which hostages take on the ideology of their captors."

Others are wary of the environmental economists who have risen to prominence in the Third Wave. David Brower, long-time leader of the Sierra Club and Friends of the Earth, once called economics "an advanced form of brain disease." To him, and to many other environmentalists, economics is a tool of business, of the opposition, a tool often used to justify stinting pollution control.

But EDF's Krupp insists that the Third Wave doesn't mean compromise. And he praises Third Wave economists for envisioning new, and often more powerful, means to traditional environmental ends. In pollution prevention, for example, "economic incentives can prod people to do the right thing in the first place, rather than requiring a complex regulatory system that brings in costly cleanup as an afterthought."

Of course, the new tools aren't exclusively financial. California's Proposition 65—authored largely by EDF's David Roe and pushed to enactment by a host of environmental groups—requires public disclosure of significant health risks from toxic chemicals. The law has created powerful incentives for industry to police its own use of hazardous substances and to resolve regulatory disputes promptly.

Third Wave enthusiasts believe that unconventional approaches can dispel tension between economic growth and environmental protection. As Krupp wrote in *The Wall Street Journal*, "The American public does not want conflict between improving our economic well-being and preserving our health and natural resources. The early experience suggests it can have both."

As a leading exponent of Third Wave thinking, EDF has worked on problems from the grass roots to the stratosphere. Its footprints are all around us. What follows are a few of them.

GETTING THE LEAD OUT

Ever since EDF was spawned in the battle against DDT use in Suffolk County, Long Island, the control of toxic substances has remained a central goal of its work. The group has fought to curb or ban uses of a range of hazardous materials from TRIS—the cancer-causing flame retardant once found in children's sleepwear—to toxic heavy metals. In the case of hazardous wastes, EDF has pressed government and industry to provide for the true costs of safe handling and final disposal.

The group has also tried to harness industry initiative to the control of toxics. Today, EDF staffers are using both traditional regulatory techniques and new approaches to protect the public from toxic materials. Here are a few of their stories.

It was only Ellen Silbergeld's second day at the Environmental Defense Fund, and already she was angry.

Christopher DeMuth, the Office of Management and Budget official in charge of environmental affairs, had come to speak at an EDF luncheon that morning in 1982. He was a leader of the Reagan administration's drive to roll back health and safety regulation. And addressing EDF, he refused to pull punches.

There was no need to continue regulating lead content in gasoline, DeMuth told the group. Lead emissions from cars would automatically decline as new cars, running on lead-free gas, replaced older models. Refiners should be free to increase the amount of lead they added to leaded gasoline, he suggested.

As a professional toxicologist, Silbergeld was astonished. "I couldn't believe that somebody would propose putting more lead into any source," she recalled later, the outrage rising in her voice. "I said to myself, 'My God, this is much worse than I thought.' "

Silbergeld had done post-doctoral work at Johns Hopkins University and at the National Institutes of Health on lead's damage to the developing brain. Lead was one of the most-studied poisons in all of medicine, and Silbergeld knew as much about its hazards as practically anyone.

Later that year, when the Environmental Protection Agency proposed lifting its lead regulation, Silbergeld joined Eric Goldstein of the Natural Resources Defense Council and a host of public health experts who called for tighter—not looser—controls on lead.

In agency and congressional hearings, Silbergeld testified that even very low levels of lead exposure could impair children's intelligence. Her focus on gasoline was not misplaced. At the time, leaded fuel was contributing almost 90% of the total amount of lead released from all sources into the air. And about 1 out of 10 children in one urban study were found to have harmful amounts of lead in their blood.

Silbergeld noted that unlawful use of cheaper leaded gasoline in cars designed for lead-free fuel was undermining the "automatic lead phase-out" that DeMuth had projected from fleet turnover. Misfueling also ruined newer cars' catalytic converters, she noted, which compounded other pollution problems.

Average Blood Lead Levels and Lead Used in Gasoline Production

Average blood lead levels gradually declined as the use of leaded gasoline dropped.

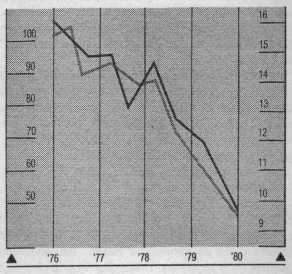

Total Lead Used Per 6 Month Period (1000 tons)	Average Blood Lead Levels (micrograms/deciliter)
Lead Used in Gasoline .... ▬	Average Blood Lead Levels .... ∿∿∿∿∿

25

Since cost-benefit analysis was the fashion, Silbergeld and EDF attorney Robert V. Percival, both trained in economics, took stabs at showing that the benefits of controlling lead would far exceed the regulations' costs. Years later, EPA's full-blown cost-benefit analysis proved Silbergeld and Percival right: lead control benefits—mostly reduced medical bills—exceeded costs by six to seven billion dollars per year.

Silbergeld was only one of scores of witnesses who weighed in for tighter lead controls. But Richard Koslowski, head of an EPA team that drafted the regulations, recalls Silbergeld as "very forceful and influential" in pressing her case.

Buttressed by stacks of testimony against lifting lead controls, EPA braved the wrath of OMB and ratcheted the standards down. In stages, the agency cut the lead allowed in gasoline by more than 90%. The results have been dramatic. From 1982 to 1987, EPA reports, annual lead emissions from vehicles dropped from 47,000 to 3,000 metric tons.

Silbergeld's entrance into the leaded gasoline debate resumed an EDF tradition. As early as 1970, EDF had petitioned the Department of Health, Education and Welfare (now Health and Human Services) to curb lead in gasoline. It had helped spur adoption of the first federal standard on lead and had called in 1973 for the complete elimination of lead from gas, a goal still not achieved.

EDF also helped to enact and implement laws to regulate other toxic substances and prevent them from contaminating drinking water. The group took special action on PCB's, asbestos, and dioxins.

These efforts have yielded important public health benefits, says Dr. Irving J. Selikoff, professor emeritus of environmental medicine at Mount Sinai School of Medicine and an EDF trustee. "Removing lead from gasoline alone may be preventing tens of thousands of cases of lead poisoning in children annually, and asbestos control will appreciably lessen our cancer burden."

But for Silbergeld, lead remains a deep frustration. Despite progress toward eliminating lead from paint and gasoline, the goal of ending childhood lead poisoning is still evasive. Medical science keeps uncovering health damage from ever lower exposure levels. Silbergeld says, "We aren't getting ahead of the problem."

Lead remains in drinking water, cans, ceramic glazes, solder, and other products that inevitably release their lead burden to the world. Rather than wage a battle product-by-product, Silbergeld and EDF attorney Karen Florini are developing a package of market-based controls on lead as a way to reduce non-essential uses of the metal while making it too valuable to throw away. The new approach, Silbergeld says, "would avoid ten years of analysis that EPA went through on every single use of asbestos" before banning it.

A similar vision of efficiency led EDF attorney David Roe to focus on getting the lead out of slow-moving regulatory procedures for toxic chemicals in California. For twenty years the country had piled law atop law in efforts to protect the public from toxics. But to Roe's mind, it was not working. Despite enormous amounts of effort by government and the private sector, regulators were moving too slowly toward making people safe from dangerous chemicals.

Government agencies assigned to regulate toxic substances often got tied up in seemingly-endless wrangles over what level of a chemical was unsafe and how it could be controlled. Bureaucrats faced political pressures as well as legitimate uncertainty over complex scientific issues. The law gave companies incentives to drag out the process, Roe figured, so they often did.

Roe was inspired by the success of his colleague Zach Willey, an EDF economist whose innovative ideas had changed the incentives of electric utility companies. Could a new approach invigorate toxic substance control?

A group of environmentalists had been drafting a California version of federal toxic control laws to offer as a ballot initiative in the 1986 election. It was long, complicated and, Roe thought, likely to sink into the same regulatory swamp as its federal models.

Roe figured the ballot initiative needed to be short and simple. And to work, it needed to reverse the incentive for delay. Delay should work against polluters. With other environmentalists as sounding boards, Roe drafted a simple-sounding proposal in two parts. The first established that residents had a legal right to know when they were being exposed to substances that cause cancer or birth defects. The state would compile a list of such chemicals, and companies would have to give warning when they exposed the public to them. The second part barred putting the same chemicals into drinking water, even indirectly.

For both parts, the proposal exempted amounts of chemicals so small as to pose insignificant risk. But to this simple framework, Roe added a crucial twist: to qualify for the exemption, industry would have to prove that the amount was insignificant.

More than 600,000 signatures later, the draft went on the ballot as Proposition 65. As expected, a broad spectrum of California industry bitterly opposed the initiative. But the opposition was poorly organized. Industry could have raised far more than the $6 million it spent fighting the proposal, Roe figured, but each company seemed to be waiting for others to contribute the cash.

Finances aside, industry faced a tough job. As Roe noted, "It was awfully hard to argue against the concept: don't dump carcinogens in drinking water, and don't blow them in people's faces without telling them. We kept asking, 'What are you doing now, that this law would make you stop?'"

Roe got his first look at an opposition billboard late one night in June 1986, as he was driving home from the Oakland airport. It read: "No on 65, The Toxics Initiative—Too Many Exemptions." Roe was delighted. It showed the opponents didn't dare mount a direct attack. "Chevron was telling you this law wasn't tough enough," he recalled later. "Now that just wasn't going to fly."

It did not. In November, voters approved Proposition 65 by a two-to-one margin.

Since then, warning labels have gone onto all tobacco

products; federal law had mandated them only on cigarettes. Wherever liquor, beer or wine is served, signs warn pregnant women that alcohol can cause birth defects.

In response to a September 1989 test case under Prop. 65, the Gillette Company agreed to remove cancer-causing trichloroethylene (TCE) from its popular Liquid Paper "white-out" products. The action came only three weeks after a coalition led by EDF had served notice that the products were exposing users to high levels of TCE without warning, in violation of Prop. 65.

Rather than add warning labels, Gillette agreed to reformulate the products, advertise the change, and set up a free exchange program. "The Gillette Company has acted very quickly and responsibly in finding a new way to make these products that avoids Prop. 65 chemicals," said Roe. "Every Liquid Paper user in the country will benefit." He pointed out that other products containing chemicals that pose cancer or birth defect risks will feel the same pressure to switch.

The full effects of Prop. 65 have not yet been seen. Pressed by food and grocery interests, the state temporarily exempted products regulated by the U.S. Food and Drug Administration, and pesticides are just starting to be placed on the state list of covered chemicals.

Industry has contended that broad implementation of the law would impose huge, unnecessary costs for minute public health gains, the equivalent of a nationwide 2% tax on foods.

With environmentalists challenging the state's exemption of FDA-regulated goods, grocery manufacturers led an aggressive lobbying push to get the Reagan and Bush administrations to pre-empt California from applying Prop. 65 to such products. But a Reagan White House task force, finding the industry's claims "greatly exaggerated," recommended leaving the law alone. Bush's OMB bluntly warned FDA officials not to reopen the door and risk "an embarrassment to the President."

In California, Thomas Warriner, the official in charge of implementing Prop. 65, has scoffed at industry claims that as many as 90,000 products will need warnings. He has talked of perhaps a score of consumer products being affected, none of them foods.

Roe highlights the importance of the exemption that Prop. 65 provides for chemicals present in quantities so small as to pose insignificant health risks. If other laws are already working as they should, he says, products should have no trouble meeting this requirement. But to be sure of an exemption, companies need state-certified standards on what level of each chemical poses negligible risk. So instead of dragging out the standard-setting process, he says, industry has started demanding decisions.

The proof of the incentive, Roe notes proudly, is that in the first twelve months after carcinogens were listed by the state, exemption levels were set for 34 chemicals—twice as many standards as EPA has managed to set under the Toxic Substances Control Act in the past twelve *years*.

So far, Prop. 65 has created nothing like the problems that its critics predicted. An industry spokesperson in California recently told a national conference that the law could "be useful in counteracting the *rigor mortis* that has appeared to have already occurred in key federal regulatory programs."

Roe, in another innovation, also has launched an effort to reduce the creation of toxic wastes at the source, rather than simply trying to clean up after they have been spilled. He arranged a partnership between EDF and the Metropolitan Water District of Southern California, a coming together of "old enemies" in the words of *The Los Angeles Times*. The partnership is funding plant-by-plant research to identify the potential for reducing the use of toxic solvents throughout the region.

Its report may well be the most detailed adding-up of what can be achieved by "source reduction" efforts ever compiled in the United States. EDF hopes that hard data from the field will "flesh out the source reduction idea and make it real in the eyes of the policy makers."

Roe describes these unconventional approaches as "an additional stage of evolution in EDF strategy." Other states and the federal government are watching implementation of Prop. 65, which *The Washington Post* has called "a Copernican revolution" in toxics regulation. Roe hopes it will prove a new paradigm for the nation.

THE TORTOISE AND THE SNARE

Every July, for decades, the bodies would wash up on South Carolina's beaches. Scores of drowned loggerhead turtles, some as big as a wheelbarrow, would blot the ribbon of sand between Myrtle Beach and Hilton Head.

The reason was no secret. Each year, turtle flotsom started appearing a few days after the shrimp fishing season opened. Air-breathing turtles were lumbering into shrimp nets and drowning. Shrimp fishermen, who had no use for turtles or large fish, were dumping 900 pounds of their carcasses overboard for every 100 pounds of shrimp they hauled home. Only a fraction of the dead washed up ashore.

But July 1989 was different. Volunteers combing South Carolina shores for the annual carnage almost came up empty. They found only two turtle corpses all month, compared with forty-five the previous July.

"It was the lowest number of dead turtles ever recorded" in the state for July, says Michael J. Bean, EDF's chief wildlife lawyer. "That means we saved some turtles." Bean savored the small victory. He knew that successes in his field were usually hard-earned and often ephemeral.

Bean is widely viewed as the nation's leading expert on wildlife law. His tall, lean, carefully dressed figure is a standard fixture at congressional hearings on the Endangered Species Act and other wildlife issues. His book, *The Evolution of National Wildlife Law*, is the primary reference work for lawyers in the field. The 1973 graduate of Yale Law School often represents a broad consortium of environmental groups alongside EDF, as well as advising agencies and legislators. He has been active in international talks to restrict trade in endangered and threatened animals. According to Donald Carr, chief of the U.S. Justice Department's wildlife section, "Any number of endangered species owe their continued existence to Michael Bean."

The loggerhead sea turtle had attracted Bean's attention more than a decade earlier. Its numbers had been dwindling as shrimp fishing expanded and condominiums crowded the turtles' breeding beaches in Florida, Georgia and South Carolina. In 1978, Bean had helped convince the government that loggerheads could be soon in danger of extinction, making them eligible for added protection.

By 1980, surveys showed mortality was even higher than expected for loggerheads as well as for the Gulf of Mexico's declining populations of Kemp's ridley turtles and green turtles. Bean, along with Washington's Center for Marine Conservation and several other conservation groups, pushed the Commerce Department into a crash research program. The goal: find a way to reduce the drowning of turtles in shrimp nets.

There was an obvious precedent. In the mid-1970's, responding to a lawsuit filed by EDF attorney William Butler, the Commerce Department had reduced porpoise drownings by ordering U.S. tuna boats to use special nets and fishing techniques. With pressure from Bean and others over the next decade, that initiative cut porpoise deaths in U.S. nets by 90%, eventually saving more than 275,000 porpoises annually.

For turtles, Commerce Department technicians refined

a gadget that some shrimpers had invented to shunt aside large jellyfish that sometimes crowded shrimp out of their nets. They dubbed it the "turtle excluder device," or TED.

A shrimp net forms a long, conical sieve with a closed end. A typical net tapers from a 50-foot-wide mouth to a narrow sac about 100 feet astern. The TED is installed in the neck of the sac. It is a large box with a grate that slants back and up to a trap door on a spring. Bars on the grate are spaced widely enough to let shrimp flow freely into the sac. But large fish and turtles bump against the bars and are deflected upward through the hinged door into the open sea.

Bean claimed the gadget would benefit shrimpers as well as turtles, reducing the drag of the net and cutting time wasted sorting out unwanted "trash" fish and turtles from shrimp. It cost between $40 and $300, a fraction of the cost of a $1000 net. And research indicated that it didn't lower the shrimp catch by much, if at all.

But shrimp fishermen didn't share Bean's enthusiasm. Some claimed they lost shrimp, others objected on principle to government meddling. Efforts to encourage voluntary use of the devices foundered. By 1986, it was evident that persuasion wasn't going to carry the day for TED's.

Bean was prepared to demand that the government impose TED's on shrimp captains. But to avoid a direct clash, he and other environmental advocates negotiated for months with fishermen over how the rules should be written. Eventually five of the six associations of shrimp fishermen agreed to a draft proposal, which the Commerce Department adopted.

How a TED Works

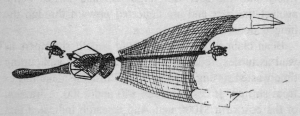

Shrimp easily pass through the TED's widely spaced bars into the closed end of the net. But when sea turtles encounter these upward-slanting bars, the current pushes them up through a trap door and safely out of the net.

Illustration by Jill Perry, © 1986 Center for Marine Conservation

The new rules took effect in time for the 1989 fishing season. Bean credited them for the sharp drop in turtle deaths off South Carolina. "It demonstrated that TED's in fact work," he said.

Yet his satisfaction lasted only a few weeks. By August, the new federal rules had been thrown overboard.

Leading the opposition was Tee John Mialjevich, populist president of the Concerned Shrimpers of Louisiana. His group was the sole dissenter from the consensus on TED rules. Returning to the Gulf Coast, he told a series of rallies that fat-cat owners of shrimp fleets and processors had sold out the small-time shrimp boat operator. Cajun country shrimpers proved a ready audience. One rally in Thibodaux, Louisiana—population 17,000—drew a raucous crowd of five thousand shrimpers and supporters. Mialjevich found receptive ears beyond his state, too. As he trawled for members in ports around the Gulf and into the South Atlantic, his group became the Concerned Shrimpers of America.

As the backlash against TED's grew, some protests turned violent. Shrimp boats blockaded several ports, including Houston-Galveston, Brownsville, and Corpus Christi, Texas. A wrench was hurled through a window of one U.S. Coast Guard cutter. Shrimpers attempted to ram Coast Guard vessels and threatened to kill anyone who tried to board their boats.

Commerce Secretary Robert Mosbacher, pressured by Gulf Coast lawmakers, withdrew the TED mandate in July. As an alternative, he allowed shrimpers to limit the time their nets stayed in the water.

That didn't satisfy Bean. The time limit would cut turtle drownings by only 20%, he figured, compared to almost 100% with TED's. And enforcement would be a nightmare, with four Coast Guard vessels policing about 15,000 shrimpers in the Gulf of Mexico. TED use was still required by state mandates in South Carolina and Florida. But even those faced uncertain futures. So EDF joined the National Wildlife Federation in a lawsuit that challenged Mosbacher's reversal.

In September, 1989, Mosbacher reversed fields again, agreeing with EDF that TED's were necessary. Despite that success, Bean, mindful of the history of this controversy, predicts that a long battle still lies ahead.

"You always try to solve a problem in a way that will satisfy as many diverse interests as possible," Bean said. "When that can't be attained, I think it is the responsibility of groups like EDF to make clear that they are prepared to file a lawsuit and butt heads. EDF is taken seriously largely because we have the capability of playing the role of courtroom adversary, and do it effectively."

THROWING IT ALL AWAY

Environmentally, recycling is the best way to dispose of many materials. It can avoid pollution, save energy, and conserve natural resources. As landfill costs have soared and incinerators have proved hard to site and operate, many cities and towns have turned to recycling to shrink their growing trash disposal problem.

To promote the trend, EDF prevailed upon the Ad Council, the advertising industry's public service arm, to launch a nationwide pro-recycling ad campaign. The theme: "If you're not recycling, you're throwing it all away."

Still, recycling has often stumbled on the charge that it cannot pay its own way. EDF, convinced that it could, has set out to prove it in a tough laboratory: New York City.

The Big Apple faces a looming trash disposal crisis. Having closed all but one of its landfills, it is currently piling about 25,000 tons of trash a day on the last of them, Staten Island's Fresh Kills. This mountain of trash will soon become the highest point on the East Coast south of Maine, and it will exhaust its capacity around the turn of the century.

To replace Fresh Kills, the city has proposed building five large trash incinerators at a capital cost of about $1.5 billion. EDF has maintained that recycling, properly structured, not only has environmental benefits but also can be cheaper than incineration. EDF economic analyst John Ruston has urged the city to invest in recycling before rushing full steam ahead into the five waste-to-energy plants.

In 1985, EDF laid out its case in a cost-comparison study, *To Burn or Not to Burn*. It called for a moderate-sized recycling program as a demonstration project. Its new perspective so threatened the city's Department of Sanitation that the department orchestrated a letter-writing campaign to EDF's board of trustees.

By mid-1988, Ruston had refined the cost study. Working with computer modeler Dan Kirshner from EDF's California office, he produced an economic analysis showing that a recycling program handling 3400 tons of waste per day would cost *60% less* per ton than incineration in the city-planned facility.

EDF also began questioning government subsidies for waste-to-energy incinerators. EDF trustee George Montgomery, a managing director at the investment banking firm of Hambrecht & Quist, identified a series of subsidies including indemnity for unanticipated risk, tax-exempt financing, guaranteed supply of raw material (trash) and markets for the end product (electricity), guaranteed disposal of incinerator ash and, most important, steep "tipping" fees that incinerators could charge for accepting trash.

Generally, recyclers got nothing comparable, Montgomery told a New York State hearing. Conferring equal treatment on recycling, the investment banker concluded, would enable it to attract capital on roughly equal footing with the incinerator industry. Without a level playing field, he complained, recyclers were competing with a serious handicap.

Ruston urged that cities should openly bid for trash

TAKE A FEW MINUTES TO GO THROUGH YOUR GARBAGE.

Every Sunday, more than 500,000 trees are used to produce the 88% of newspapers that are never recycled.

We throw away enough glass bottles and jars to fill the 1,350-foot twin towers of New York's World Trade Center *every two weeks.*

Americans go through 2.5 million plastic bottles *every hour,* only a small percentage of which are now recycled.

American consumers and industry throw away enough aluminum to rebuild our entire commercial airfleet *every three months.*

Every year we dispose of *24 million tons* of leaves and grass clippings, which could be composted to conserve landfill space.

We throw away enough iron and steel to *continuously* supply all the nation's automakers.

**IF YOU'RE NOT RECYCLING ...
YOU'RE THROWING IT ALL AWAY.**

41

disposal services by issuing standard requests for proposal to all parties: recyclers, incinerators and landfills. The costs of each should be compared, including the hidden subsidies noted by Montgomery. And contracts should go to the least costly plan.

New York City's Department of Sanitation continues to press for construction of its first planned incinerator at the Brooklyn Navy Yard. EDF has said it would accede to the plant on three conditions: if it had state-of-the-art pollution control and monitoring, strict rules for ash handling and disposal, and a requirement that the city be recycling 3400 tons per day—roughly the amount of trash it plans to send to the incinerator—before the fire is lit.

After EDF put forward these same recommendations at state adjudicative hearings, the state Department of Environmental Conservation adopted strong positions on recycling and incinerator ash. In November 1988, DEC commissioner Thomas Jorling declined to issue any permit for the Brooklyn Navy Yard incinerator until the inadequacy of the city's recycling and ash disposal plans is remedied.

As the city continues to wrestle with the problem, EDF has convinced Manhattan to develop plans to create an "intensive recycling zone" in a small, diverse area of the city. The idea came from EDF general counsel James Tripp, who heads Manhattan's Citizens Advisory Council on waste disposal. Cities as diverse as Los Angeles and Seattle have set ambitious recycling goals. But New York's size and population make it a special challenge.

Tripp hopes the program will show that recycling can succeed even in the Big Apple's densely-packed core.

Another EDF initiative that has helped recycling has been its demonstration that disposal of incinerator ash will require stronger, more costly safeguards than some had believed.

Richard Denison, a biochemist with a Yale University Ph.D., worried that new waste-to-energy incinerators would concentrate toxic metals in their ash residues. Checking on the few available ash tests confirmed his suspicion. Fly ash recovered from incinerator smoke almost always contained so much toxic heavy metal that it was classed as hazardous waste. Ash from the bottom of furnaces reached the hazardous range about one-third of the time.

What bothered Denison was that both kinds of ash were routinely dumped in ordinary landfills, notorious for leaking toxics into groundwater. Incinerator ash had even been scattered on icy roads to improve traction.

In 1987, he and EDF attorney Robert Percival informed one hundred incinerator operators of the findings, and asserted that the law required them to test their ash and send it to hazardous waste landfills if it tested hazardous.

At that, "all hell broke loose," recalls Denison.

Mayors and incinerator-makers clamored for help. Cities, which operated most incinerators, feared that they would face sharply higher costs and liability if they had to play by hazardous-waste rules. Under federal law, hazardous waste requires greater care in handling and shipping and must be disposed of in special landfills. Citizen opposition and difficulty in getting permits have made hazardous waste disposal facilities rare and costly. New Jersey toxic wastes, for instance, are being trucked to Ohio facilities. The cost of using such facilities would turn incinerators overnight into high-tech white elephants.

The industry claimed that Congress had intended to exempt incinerators from the hazardous waste law, but EDF believed otherwise. In a meeting with then-EPA administrator Lee Thomas and a subsequent legal brief, EDF persistently underscored the public health and legal consequences of improper ash management, eventually convincing EPA to rebuff the industry claim.

Turning up the heat, EDF sued two mass-burn incinerators, calling for proper disposal of the ash. In an effort to span the spectrum, it selected a new, fairly efficient plant owned and operated by Wheelabrator Technologies, Inc., in Westchester County, New York; and an older incinerator owned by the City of Chicago.

Denison hoped the suits would bring the incinerator industry and cities to the negotiating table to craft a legislative solution. "We didn't view the hazardous waste rules as necessarily the best way to handle incinerator ash," he says. "Taking New Jersey's ash to Ohio dumps never seemed to me to be a viable long-term option." Instead, Denison argued for creating landfills solely for incinerator ash, equipped with double liners, monitoring, and recovery of liquid leachate.

In fact, while federal action has been contentious and as yet inconclusive, EDF "is getting most of what it wants from the states," Denison says. A dozen states are developing or have adopted rules that would send incinerator ash to specially-equipped landfills.

At first, Michael Oppenheimer thought the letter might be a practical joke. British Prime Minister Margaret Thatcher was inviting him to brief her and her ministers on global warming. Sure, and after that, President Gorbachev wanted to visit him in New York, right?

But the invitation proved genuine, and clearly, this opportunity to brief a world leader was not to be missed.

So on April 26, 1989, Oppenheimer walked into 10 Downing Street. In a wood-panelled room there, he joined a score of other scientists, a half-dozen cabinet ministers and Britain's Iron Lady herself. For six and a half hours, Thatcher listened and asked questions as scientists explained and discussed the greenhouse effect, which threatens to raise average temperatures as much as eight degrees fahrenheit in the next century.

For Oppenheimer, one of only two Americans invited, the meeting was "unbelievable."

"I spend all my life trying to indirectly influence somebody, hoping to get Bush's attention through someone else. Here I could come up to Mrs. Thatcher and I could say, 'Prime Minister...,' and if that conversation didn't work well I could go up to her again."

Oppenheimer seized four chances to make points personally to Thatcher during tea breaks and informal discussions. "It is unlikely I'll ever get such an opportunity again," he said, "at least not with Mrs. Thatcher."

Nothing could better illustrate the climate change in Oppenheimer's work. For much of the past five years, the tall, bearded astrophysicist had toiled in the shadows, trying to raise evidence about the greenhouse effect into the glare of public and political concern. He had prodded news reporters, waded into TV talk shows, organized conferences for scientists and politicians, testified endlessly before congressional committees.

While talk of global environmental issues slowly advanced in scientific circles, it seemed to make politicians' eyes glaze over. "At the international level, nobody could agree to do anything except sign the law of the sea treaty, which didn't work," complains Oppenheimer.

The 1985 discovery of a seasonal "hole" of thinning ozone over Antarctica changed the political atmosphere. Ozone in the upper atmosphere is crucial, for it shields the earth from cancer-causing ultraviolet radiation. Stratospheric ozone is being eroded by man-made chemicals, principally substances called chlorofluorocarbons (CFC's) and halons that are used as coolants, solvents and plastic foam bubbling agents. Most of the same gases also contribute to the greenhouse effect.

By 1987, scores of nations had signed a protocol that called for sharp curbs on the use of ozone-depleting CFC's and halons. Two years later, pressures were rising to phase them out altogether by the end of the century.

Global warming was fast becoming a hot issue too. With green parties in Europe gaining strength, politicians were competing to lead on global environmental issues. Thatcher called for a global convention on the greenhouse effect. French president Francois Mitterand was hosting a conference on it. U.S. President George Bush expanded his call for an exploratory workshop to include a policy-making convention. Even Soviet leader Mikhail Gorbachev, who cultivated green parties' support for disarmament efforts, was showing interest.

That Oppenheimer was sucked into the vortex was no accident. He put himself there. In 1981, he had left a tenured astrophysics research position at the Harvard-Smithsonian Observatory to work on atmospheric pollution problems at the Environmental Defense Fund. From the start, he sought to build the scientific and popular basis for a government crackdown on acid rain pollutants. But global warming kept grabbing his attention.

Warming moved to the top of his agenda in 1985. Armed with two foundation grants, Oppenheimer began working with the Beijer Institute, a think tank in Stockholm, Sweden, to stimulate public debate and international action on the greenhouse issue.

Scientific discussion of a possible greenhouse effect went back to the 19th century. The idea was that the buildup of carbon dioxide (CO_2) and certain other gases in the atmosphere would act like a greenhouse roof over the earth, trapping more of the sun's heat.

Early in this century, concerns were mollified by evidence that the oceans were absorbing carbon dioxide. But in the 1950's and 1960's, scientists found that CO_2 had been building up in the atmosphere. One scientist projected that when concentration of the gas doubled in the next century, surface temperatures would rise an average of about four degrees fahrenheit.

Slowly, a consensus emerged that the forecasts were understated; temperatures could rise about twice that amount, which would be the biggest jump in human history. New deserts could spread across the mid-latitudes. With polar ice melting and oceans warming, sea levels could rise as much as three feet in a century, inundating coastal lowlands.

The average American paid little heed to the building scientific consensus; but in the summer of 1988, the tinder of public opinion was dry and brittle. The media were full of stories of a farm belt drought. Dust-bowl analogies choked the airwaves. On a slow news day on a sweltering August morning, TV cameras crowded into a Senate committee chamber to catch a hearing on what appeared a remote, speculative subject: global climate change.

James Hansen, head of NASA's Goddard Institute for Space Study, threw the lighted match onto the tinder. Pointing to the oppressive heat outside as a sample of things to come, he said the greenhouse effect is here. The earth's warming has already begun.

Suddenly, global warming appeared on TV news shows and magazine covers. No one was happier than Oppenheimer. For five years he had struggled to interest reluctant policymakers and an indifferent public in the greenhouse effect. Finally, the light of public attention was glaring in his face.

The Senate hearing that Hansen addressed had been scheduled largely to hear about policy recommendations from the international workshops that Oppenheimer had helped to organize. His own contribution to the global warming debate, Oppenheimer explained, was partly to "provide a track for getting the policy train moving."

Oppenheimer also functioned as kind of an interpreter for the scientific community. Scientists tend to be cautious and technical about stating their conclusions.

Oppenheimer had a blue-chip background as a scientist. With his balding pate and dark beard, he looked like the kind of brooding genius that might emerge from a lab with startling findings. But he was a born communicator. He was adept at simplifying scientific jargon, dressing it in compelling imagery and fitting it into sweeping concepts.

In his meeting with Thatcher, for instance, Oppenheimer seized every chance to stress one of his favorite themes, lag time. Greenhouse gases have been building up in the atmosphere for centuries as man has burned increasing quantities of wood, coal, and oil for fuel. But the full warming effect of the buildup takes decades to be felt. So even if release of so-called greenhouse gases were to end today, past loadings could spur more warming well into the next century.

The point was crucial to combat arguments that the world can wait for irrefutable scientific proof of a serious warming trend. "We can't wait," Oppenheimer told Thatcher. She absorbed the point, he recalled, "She started talking about a lag."

At EDF, Oppenheimer has taken time for carefully-selected scientific research and writing. "Scientists are funny," he explains. "They pick things that are interesting scientifically; I pick things that are interesting from a policy perspective."

He has published peer-reviewed papers on subjects ranging from acid rain to greenhouse warming impacts. "I have to keep doing research and publishing," Oppenheimer says, or, "in the end, no one would listen to me."

Today, Oppenheimer leads an expanding EDF effort on a range of international environmental problems.

EDF economist Dr. Daniel Dudek has published analyses of policy options to moderate the growth of both CFC's and CO_2. One Dudek study found that the cost of curbing CFC use was a mere fraction of the avoided costs that would otherwise stem from these chemicals' damage to the ozone layer and their contribution to climate change. Another of his reports showed that it may be economically viable to require fossil-fuel-burning industries to plant trees to recapture as much CO_2 as their plants emit. EDF has even suggested that industrial nations might pay countries like Brazil to preserve their tropical rainforests as global storehouses of CO_2.

Recently, Oppenheimer has been working with EDF scientists Mary Voytek and Dr. Rod Fujita on studies of mechanisms that could slow or speed the rate of greenhouse warming. Fujita, with a Boston University Ph.D. in marine biology, is studying how salt marshes, seaweed beds and coral reefs could affect global warming. Voytek, a biologist specializing in the interactions among ocean species, has probed whether microscopic plant life in Antarctic waters would capture more or less CO_2 in a warming ocean exposed to more ultraviolet light.

On a less theoretical plane, EDF attorney-scientist Bruce Manheim has also been monitoring the Antarctic region, which has become a sort of international laboratory for assessing the effects of ozone depletion.

Since 1981, EDF has been the only non-governmental U.S. representative to the international body that sets limits on fishing and other activities affecting Antarctic species.

Manheim has become the icy continent's muckraker. He filmed Soviet trawlers breaking an international agreement limiting fishing near South Georgia Island, a shipwrecked Argentine vessel leaking 170,000 gallons of diesel fuel off the U.S. Palmer Station, and penguins picking their way through a trash dump at the Argentines' Esperanza base.

Manheim didn't spare the United States. His 1988 white paper, *On Thin Ice*, documented that U.S. scientific bases, established to study the pristine continent, were carelessly polluting it. That paper, together with film and protests from Greenpeace, helped prod the National Science Foundation to launch a $30 million program to treat sewage, replace open pit burning with controlled incineration, and ship home discarded plastics and other materials.

"Antarctic politics move at literally a glacial pace," Manheim says, and forcing the U.S. cleanup was the first step toward prodding other nations to match it.

Long lead times and careful preparation are earmarks of most of EDF's international work. Today, Oppenheimer is working on policy options to combat the greenhouse effect that will be discussed in an international meeting before the end of 1990. Manheim is working toward a crucial round of talks in 1991 on renegotiating the international treaty governing Antarctica.

Oppenheimer looks ahead with optimism, encouraged by the relatively quick international action on CFC's and the rise of interest in global warming.

"It is no exaggeration," he wrote boldly in *The New*

York Times, "to say that global environment may become the overarching issue for the next forty years in the way the cold war defined our world view during the last forty years."

He shrugs off suggestions that the greenhouse problem is too fundamental or complex to be solved by nations. Pointing out that the world has rapidly switched energy usage in the past—by necessity—he insists it can do so again, by design.

"Fighting the cold war has actually shaped the way our industrial development occurred in the past forty years," he observes. "So to say that governments can't force these changes is ridiculous."

UP IN SMOKE

In heavily forested Northwest Brazil, an 1100-mile road has opened up the states of Rondonia and North Mato Grasso for settlement by Brazil's fast-growing population. But instead of a showcase for progress, the World Bank-funded Polonoroeste project has become a symbol of man's folly.

A half-million peasants have streamed into the wilderness, drawn by the promise of free land around well-equipped villages. But the forest's thin soils can't sustain their crops for more than a few years. Villages lack medical care, teachers and agricultural support. In desperation, tens of thousands move on, setting the ancient forest ablaze to clear new land, repeating the cycle of human impoverishment and ecological destruction.

This roadbuilding project in the world's largest tropical rainforest is "an environmental catastrophe and an economic debacle," says Bruce Rich, a senior EDF attorney based in Washington. And after years of weathering criticism from Rich and his allies, the World Bank now agrees.

The bank's president, Barber Conable, concedes that Polonoroeste "went wrong." The bank, he has said, "misread the human, institutional and physical realities of the jungle and the frontier."

Conable's reversal was seen as no small change in the world of multilateral development banks (MDB's). Gus Speth, president of the World Resources Institute, a leading Washington center for policy research, immediately spotted it as "a turning point in the World Bank's approach to the environment." Speth went on to say, "A large share of the credit for this new departure at the World Bank must go to Bruce Rich and his colleagues in the 'MDB coalition.'"

Rich and EDF anthropologist Dr. Stephan Schwartzman had doggedly researched the most questionable MDB projects, forming a network among affected Brazilians, Indians and Indonesians. They delivered firsthand reports to environmental groups in the U.S., Europe and Scandinavia, news media, and key members of Congress. The resulting furor broke even the World Bank's celebrated imperturbability.

Today, Rich and Schwartzman are regularly consulted by the World Bank and the Inter-American Development Bank regarding environmental and social effects of international lending. The banks, embarrassed by past mistakes, have expanded their own environmental analysis and assigned it new prominence. Some dubious projects have been revised, delayed or denied loans. Seldom have so few people sparked revolutionary change in such proud and powerful institutions.

Bruce Rich has spent six years fighting Polonoroeste, yet the litany still stirs him to anger. It was so *predictable*, he complains.

Multilateral banks have repeatedly helped finance large-scale agricultural resettlement and colonization projects in pristine tropical forests. Almost without exception, says Rich, these have been disasters.

The problem? The poor soils of Polonoroeste, ill-suited for farming, are typical of tropical forests. Settlements lie far from markets and supplies. Pesticides and fertilizer are difficult to obtain and use; disease and pest infestations often prove hard to control.

The Amazon has long been a magnet for grandiose schemes: the jungle is littered with the wreckage of exotic ventures. In the 1920's and 30's, Ford Motor Company tried to turn a Connecticut-sized plot into a rubber plantation. In the 1960's and 70's, billionaire Daniel Ludwig attempted to develop an enormous tree farm for paper production. Both retreated in frustration with huge losses.

Such ventures have aroused environmentalists' concern for decades. Tropical deforestation threatens the survival of more than half the planet's plant and animal species. Botanists warn of the loss of undiscovered plants with medical, agricultural and industrial uses; dozens of important drugs that cannot be chemically synthesized already come from tropical plants incapable of growing elsewhere. Recently, scientists have added new fears: carbon dioxide buildup could cause a warming of the earth's atmosphere unprecedented in human history. Burning of the great forests of the developing world is a major source of the added carbon dioxide.

The tropical forests' demise caught Rich's attention in 1980, when he read warnings about species destruction while a law student at the University of Pennsylvania. Rich had mastered six languages while teaching and traveling in Latin America and Europe. He had been appalled by the rainforest destruction he had witnessed in Latin America. So after law school, Rich joined the Natural Resources Defense Council's international program. He started promoting forest protection within the

U.S. Agency for International Development and the United Nations Environment Program.

But Rich remained restless. In the early 1980's, military dictatorships in nations like Brazil and Indonesia shrugged off environmental appeals. They deeply resented outside interference. They were bent on developing resources and generating exports, even if only for short-term gains, to pay interest on mounting foreign debts. Often their projects also had social, political or national security goals, Rich noted, such as dispersing landless peasants from urban areas.

International conferences of concerned environmentalists frustrated this enterprising dynamo of a lawyer. "It was the converted talking to the converted," Rich recalls. "The meetings and papers had no impact on people who had power to change things."

Rich decided to focus on the multilateral development banks—primarily the World Bank and the Inter-American Development Bank—which clearly had the power, if not the inclination, to change things. These giants churned out billions of dollars yearly to less developed countries, often for environmentally harmful projects. And their endorsement became the green light for dozens of private international banks to pour their own cash into projects.

At the time, multilateral banks were lending to two major schemes to colonize pristine tropical forests. One was Polonoroeste. Rich thought he could make the case that such projects made no sense, not just environmentally, but also *economically*.

"We began to look at the performance records of these kinds of projects in the last forty years in Latin America.

And what we discovered was that almost uniformly these projects failed. But each time you had multilateral development agencies saying, with tremendous technological hubris, 'Well, the planners didn't realize what they were dealing with. But this time we will make it work.' "

Despite the banks' sorry record, taking them on was a daunting task. The World Bank's professional staff of 3,000 was reputedly the world's leading repository of expertise on Third World development. Its prestige and influence were enormous. Who was Rich to second-guess it?

But Rich knew the banks' Achilles' heel: political pressure from the countries that funded them, principally the United States. Getting information to the right politicians, he reasoned, could generate constructive pressure on the banks.

Rich expanded his network of contacts worldwide. He used it to collect and disseminate research on problematic bank projects. He wrote articles and letters and made himself a regular witness at congressional hearings. Most important, he formed a powerful alliance with a U.S. senator who adopted his cause with enthusiasm.

The alliance stemmed from the World Bank's curt dismissal of a research report and letter calling for action to fix specific problems on the Polonoroeste project. Rich had backed the letter with endorsements from 50 environmental groups and Brazilian organizations.

Rich took the bank's brusque response to Senator Robert Kasten, a conservative Republican from Wisconsin who chaired the Senate appropriations subcommittee that acted on World Bank funding. Kasten hit the roof.

In an angry letter, Kasten scolded World Bank president A.W. Clausen, saying that the environmentalists had "raised a number of legitimate concerns"—and potential solutions—only to get an insulting brush-off. Incredibly, Kasten made a veiled threat to slash the United States' 20% funding of the bank.

The senator also sent a letter to then-Treasury Secretary Donald Regan, who was in charge of overseeing U.S. voting within the multilateral banks.

The missives met their objective. When the Inter-American Development Bank considered a $72 million loan to extend the highway from Rondonia into the neighboring Brazilian state of Acre (pronounced ah-cray), the bank's U.S. director abstained on environmental grounds. It was the first time such a move had ever been made. And while it blocked only one-fifth of the funds, it served notice to multilateral banks that the U.S. would not rubber-stamp destructive projects.

By that time, attitudes at the multilateral banks were beginning to change. When Rich had met with the World Bank's Clausen early in 1984, Clausen had lectured him, "Don't hold the World Bank hostage to the environment," adding testily, "I resent the leverage."

When Rich next visited the World Bank president in 1985, he went with Kasten, and the change in the bank's attitude was palpable.

With the senator's help, Rich had demanded a discussion of the Polonoroeste project with the bank's Brazilian experts and top officials. This time, the bank's wood-panelled board room was crowded with four World Bank vice presidents, most of its Brazil staff, and representatives from the State and Treasury Departments, as well

Rainforest Fires

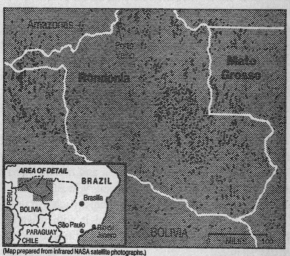

(Map prepared from infrared NASA satellite photographs.)

One factor contributing to the global greenhouse effect is the widespread burning of tropical rainforests. This map, detailing most of the Polonoroeste project area, was prepared from infrared satellite photographs showing 6000 manmade fires in the Amazon forest in a single day.

Source: NASA, 1988.

as other environmentalists and Senator Kasten and his staff.

Clausen opened the meeting cordially. Then Rich launched into a detailed discussion of Polonoroeste with the bank's Brazil staff. The bank had held up cash for the project until emergency environmental planning was done. Rich kept emphasizing the need to protect Indian reserves and slow the settler influx, which Brazil was pumping up with nationwide ads touting "the new El Dorado." The meeting lasted three hours. Clausen probably still resented it, but it was apparent that Rich had increased his leverage.

Rich moved from NRDC to EDF during 1985, and continued building critical pressure on the World Bank. On Easter Sunday, 1987, Polonoroeste criticism peaked with a devastating portrayal on CBS television's "60 Minutes." Film of forest destruction and human misery alternated with interviews with an angry Senator Kasten and uncomfortable World Bank officials. Rich had prodded CBS to do the story and armed it with research, including documents from the project's critics inside the World Bank.

By then, Clausen was gone and Conable had swept into the World Bank presidency with a broad new agenda. A few weeks after the "60 Minutes" broadcast, Conable made his extraordinary admission of error on Polonoroeste, and committed to beef up the bank's environmental analysis.

Up to that time, by Rich's count, only three World Bank officials had been responsible for reviewing the environmental impact of more than 300 new projects a year, as well as hundreds of ongoing projects. One solitary employee had reviewed all projects in agriculture, energy and transportation, which made up about half of the bank's lending in recent years.

Conable pledged to elevate the environmental staff to a department, boosted its staffing from 17 to 60, and established environmental units in all four regional offices. He launched a review of environmental problems in thirty developing countries. And he promised to bring a new mindset to the bank.

"If the World Bank has been part of the problem in the past, I intend to make it a leader for finding solutions for the future," Conable said. "Sound ecology is good economics."

With Conable atop the World Bank and Kasten watching him like a guard dog, Rich started finding the bank more responsive to his efforts to slow funding of the bank's other major rainforest colonization scheme, Indonesia's "Transmigration" project.

The costly program was designed to shuffle more than one million people from the crowded islands of Java and Bali to the sparsely-populated forests of Borneo and New Guinea. It was supposed to employ the poor and develop wilderness. But Rich found that there were strong disagreements within the World Bank, and even the Indonesian government itself, over the wisdom of the program. One report, endorsed by four Indonesian ministries, said that 300,000 resettled people were living in grinding poverty. To be sure, about half of all those moved reported being better off. But many isolated and inexperienced farmers went hungry working thin soils in the settlements. Some were making their way back to Java.

Rich contended that there were less costly and destructive means of attaining the goals of Transmigration. Labor-intensive light export industries on Java would create jobs, he claimed, and birth-control campaigns could more cheaply relieve overcrowding.

Rich frequently found ammunition inside the World Bank. When internal critiques of Transmigration were leaked to him, they often triggered letters to the bank co-signed by dozens of groups in his network of allies.

On one occasion, Rich asked Ernest Stern, the number-two man at the bank, why it didn't drop Transmigration funding. Stern's response, Rich recalls, was that the project was a major priority of Indonesia; it was going to happen anyway, everyone assumed, so by being involved, the World Bank could have a positive impact.

The comment outraged Rich. "By that argument," he snapped, "the bigger the project and the more flawed it is, the greater the justification for the World Bank's involvement."

Late in 1987, under prodding from the World Bank, the Indonesian government quietly came around. Rather than financing new colonization sites, it would consolidate existing settlements to make them sustainable.

———————

Rainforest colonization can devastate indigenous peoples. Few Americans have witnessed this as closely as Rich's EDF colleague Dr. Stephan Schwartzman.

Schwartzman wrote his Ph.D. dissertation on a tribe literally decimated in a single decade by disease and conflict with colonists. Of the original 900 Indians, only 85 survived to be moved 1,000 miles south to a new home in Xingu National Park.

Schwartzman has championed Indians and rubber tappers, who live off the forest largely by harvesting its rubber and nuts. He brought rubber-tapper leader Chico Mendes to the United States to speak to multilateral bank officials and members of Congress. Schwartzman and a colleague also conducted research suggesting that the rubber tappers actually produced more income and greater exports for remote Acre than farming or cattle ranching. Their report popularized the rubber tappers' notion of creating "extractive reserves," where the forest would be preserved for rubber and nut gathering.

World Bank officials praised the extractive reserves concept. They and Inter-American Development Bank officials called for such reserves in projects they supported. Even the governor of Acre backed them. By 1989, twelve of the reserves had been created, covering five million acres of forest, and more are expected in the Polonoroeste area.

But even this small victory was stained by the brutal violence that forest settlement projects spawn. Chico Mendes was murdered on December 23, 1988, apparently because his efforts to protect the rainforest posed a threat to cattle-ranching interests.

Today, EDF's Rich, Schwartzman and attorney Lori Udall continue to research and monitor more than twenty multilateral bank-funded projects, ranging from a charcoal-fired pig iron plant in Brazil to hydroelectric dams in India. They have won better treatment for displaced people and helped to involve affected populations in project planning.

Rich now is turning his spotlight on the World Bank's alter ego, the International Monetary Fund. The IMF imposes often-draconian economic reforms in return for large loans to countries suffering balance of payments problems. Rich and his allies are beginning to demand broader environmental review to ensure that IMF prescriptions don't accept long-term ecological destruction as the price of short-term exports.

Rich and Schwartzman worry that Barber Conable's proposed turnabout at the World Bank remains largely unfulfilled. They cite institutional resistance within the bank, understaffing of its environmental department and circumvention of that department by the bank's regional offices. Yet significant change has occurred. The rhetoric of multilateral banks has reversed itself, and while environmental planning doesn't dominate the World Bank, it clearly looms larger in loan evaluations.

Two years ago, Senator Kasten noted the change as Rich testified one more time on bank lending. "I think you, as much as any other single person, are responsible for the efforts and the progress that we are making," the senator said. "We're not there yet, but we have come a long, long way."

THE GRAY TRIANGLE:
ACID OVER THE WEST

Was a cloud going to follow Robert Yuhnke wherever he went? Acid rain, after all, had been drenching the Northeast, threatening lakes and forests, while he worked in Pennsylvania as Assistant Attorney General for the Department of Environmental Resources. And it wasn't until Yuhnke moved to the EDF office in Boulder, Colorado, that anyone had thought of acid rain as a Western problem as well.

Now he was frustrated. Knowing the chemistry of acid deposition, Yuhnke for three years had warned that smoke from a few Southwestern copper smelters threatened to acidify thousands of Rocky Mountain lakes. But few people had taken him seriously.

And in mid-1984, Yuhnke was facing evidence that could silence him. The Wyoming Department of Environmental Quality was saying that acid rain in the state's Wind River range fell far short of the amount that Yuhnke himself believed would create any problems. If the department was right, he was the one blowing smoke.

It didn't make sense, Yuhnke thought as he pored over federal data on acid deposition in the Rockies. The measurements from 1981 had been *twice as high* as the state's figures from just two years later. Why?

Suddenly, the explanation hit him. Acid fallout was low in 1983 because a strike had shut down the region's copper smelters for three months that year. Back in 1981, with the copper industry booming, deposition had reached harmful levels. Now, with the strike over and a huge new Mexican smelter due to boost the area's sulfur emissions by 25% in the next few years, Yuhnke figured the region was in for a shock. "We've found the smoking gun," he said to himself.

What Yuhnke had found, in fact, was the first element of proof that rising emissions of sulfur could cause proportionate increases in acid rain hundreds of miles downwind. And that was just the proof that then-President Ronald Reagan insisted that environmentalists were lacking when they called for federal action on acid rain.

————————

In the East, where many power plants burned high-sulfur coal, concerns about acid rain had been growing for more than a decade.

Federal air pollution rules had been written primarily to protect people's health near polluting plants. So instead of forcing plants to clean up their smoke, regulators let many of them shoot it skyward through taller and taller stacks. While that did minimize smoke locally, it also launched pollutants high into the atmosphere, where they were changed chemically into acids and often traveled long distances before falling back to earth as acid rain or snow. Some Northeastern precipitation had the pH of vinegar.

High-altitude lakes from New York's Adirondacks through Nova Scotia were the first to show the effects. As acids built up in the water, fish and other marine life died out. Meanwhile, acid rain ate away at buildings and monuments. It leached toxic metals into some water supplies and was found capable of altering the chemistry of soils. At the same time, forest damage was seen to be increasing, though scientists differed over the extent of the damage and the degree to which it stemmed from other air pollutants.

What made the causes of acid rain difficult to study in the East was that there were hundreds of sources of pollution spread over a very large area, with relatively little change from year to year in the amount of emissions. In the intermountain West, there were only a few sources—large copper smelters—and Yuhnke had discovered very large changes in emissions. "Such large variations," his study noted, "can be thought of as representing an unintentional experiment on the atmosphere that could not be performed readily in the eastern United States."

Working with EDF scientists Dr. Michael Oppenheimer and Charles B. Epstein, Yuhnke plotted four years of sulfate fallout levels in Rocky Mountain rain, fog and snow. The team then charted sulfur dioxide emissions from ten Southwestern smelters for the same period. The lines zigged and zagged almost in lockstep. The acidic fallout varied directly with smelter emissions as far as 1000 miles away.

Their study was accepted for publication in the August 1985 issue of *Science*, the journal of the American Association for the Advancement of Science. Its appearance effectively silenced the skeptics who had been saying that pollution from far-off power plants could not be blamed for acid damage in the Northeast and Canada. *The New York Times* reported the findings, "Distant Pollution Tied to Acid Rain," at the top of page one—

Sulfur Emissions and Sulfur in Precipitation

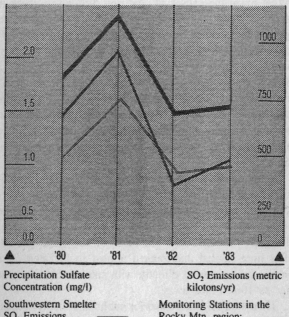

Precipitation Sulfate
Concentration (mg/l)

Southwestern Smelter
SO₂ Emissions ......

SO₂ Emissions (metric
kilotons/yr)

Monitoring Stations in the
Rocky Mtn. region:
Pawnee ....
Sand Spring ....

From "Acid Deposition, Smelter Emissions, and the Linearity Issue
in the United States," by Michael Oppenheimer, Charles B. Epstein,
and Robert E. Yuhnke.

just below the weather forecast, which called for clearing skies.

Back in the West, Yuhnke's findings reverberated far and wide. The Casper, Wyoming, *Star* prominently featured his analysis of acid rain threats to the Wind River range, and the governor appointed a task force to study the issue. Congressmen like Wyoming Representative Dick Cheney, who loved flyfishing in "the Winds," started seeking his advice. The usually cautious Forest Service supported him in Colorado. Before long, Arizona Governor Bruce Babbitt was telling the state Chamber of Commerce that the future of a healthy economy in Arizona depended on clean air.

The powerful copper industry formerly had kept regulators at bay by flexing its political muscles. But Yuhnke sensed that tolerance for copper smelters that violated pollution control laws was nearing an end. With the help of Dick Kamp, whose Smelter Crisis Project led a network of critics of polluters in the Southwest, Yuhnke laid a trap.

Bait was set about 60 miles south of the Mexican border. There, the Nacozari smelter, due to open without pollution controls in 1986, was expected to pour almost a half-million tons of sulfur dioxide a year into the sky. That was 50% more than the emissions from the worst U.S. smelter, Phelps Dodge Corporation's 70-year-old facility at Douglas, Arizona.

Drawing lines around Douglas, Nacozari, and another Mexican smelter at Cananea, environmentalists branded the region the "Gray Triangle." Politicians across the Southwest began expressing concern. Lawmakers warned that Nacozari's foreign owners, while dirtying

U.S. skies, would enjoy a competitive advantage over U.S. companies that bore heavier regulatory costs.

But those who demanded action on Nacozari soon found themselves trapped against harder decisions closer to home. Having demanded a Mexican crackdown, they could not continue delaying one here. So when EPA started pressuring the Mexicans to curb Nacozari's pollution, the writing was on the wall for heavily-polluting U.S. smelters.

Focusing on the huge, antiquated Douglas smelter, Yuhnke discovered medical tests showing that asthma sufferers living nearby could have attacks triggered by as little as one-tenth the level of sulfur dioxide that periodically filled the air. Dealing with asthmatics "changed the focus of the whole thing for me," Yuhnke was to say later. "It reduced this to personal suffering, life and death, rather than just protecting the environment."

The Douglas smelter earned only marginal profits. Phelps-Dodge pledged to close it rather than install costly new pollution controls. Governor Babbitt urged EPA to close the plant unless it complied with the law. Finally, in July 1986, EPA ordered Douglas to shut down. The huge stacks exhaled their last hot breath on January 15, 1987, and the furnaces fell silent for good.

Early the next morning, Yuhnke drove out to the plant with his leading allies in the Douglas battle: Priscilla Robinson, director of Tucson-based Southwest Environmental Service, the area's leading grass-roots group, and Kamp, who had fought the Douglas smelter for years.

As he looked up at the plant, the eerie silence chilled Yuhnke. "It was just this mountain of raw steel and girders and huge furnaces that stood ten stories tall and huge stacks that stood 960 feet high. And there was no smoke coming out of the stacks. Nothing. It had completely died."

Despite its massive size and power, the Douglas plant had been doomed by its failure to curb threats to human health and the environment. Its age and antiquated design made it unable to afford the cost of clean operation. It was a dinosaur; the climate had changed, and it had failed to adapt.

Newer plants adjusted. Nacozari installed effective, new emissions-control equipment that should reduce its sulfur emissions by 90%. The Magma Copper Corporation, after negotiating a settlement with EDF and EPA, added similar controls to its facility at San Manuel, Arizona.

These moves cut sulfur dioxide emissions in the Rocky Mountain region by more than one million tons annually, an outright reduction of 55%. Without a cap on potential new sources of pollution, however, the victory could be a fleeting one. Coal-fired power plants still threaten visibility over some national parks, and, eventually, power plant growth will revive the western acid rain threat unless utility emissions too are better controlled. Still, the gains to date should be sufficient, Yuhnke claims, to keep acid rain in the region within "tolerable levels" for perhaps a decade.

CLEARING THE AIR

The message was simple: put your money where your mouth is.

EDF's Fred Krupp had been summoned to the office of C. Boyden Gray, counsel to President-elect George Bush, who was then still Vice President.

Ushered into Gray's office in the Old Executive Office Building, Krupp sensed the excitement in the air. He had been called in on short notice. The new administration was just beginning to take shape. And Gray, who would be a key player, seemed a potential environmental ally. Gray's invitation looked like the opening that Krupp had long hoped EDF would receive.

Gray had first sought him out two years earlier, in fact, when *The Wall Street Journal* published Krupp's article on "Third Wave" environmentalism. Now, with Senators Tim Wirth and John Heinz having given Bush their bipartisan report entitled, *Project 88: Harnessing Market Forces to Protect Our Environment,* the Third Wave notions had added political credibility.

Gray and Krupp shook hands and sat down. After chatting about Presidential appointments, Gray noted that Bush intended to propose new controls on acid rain. The President-elect wanted to harness market forces to make the controls work better, as EDF had been urging. Could EDF propose how the program should work?

Krupp was ecstatic. The request had seemed almost offhand, Krupp thought, as he passed the Secret Service guards' desk and stepped out onto 17th Street, but to him it was a mandate, a chance to design the President's program.

Joseph Goffman wasn't so sure. Goffman, EDF's lead attorney on air pollution issues, carried the scars of five years of Washington environmental battles. He had grown cautious and suspicious. EDF colleagues called him, "Mr. Doom and Gloom."

At EDF's busy offices on P Street, Goffman turned over the Gray invitation in his mind. It sounded like an empty gesture. Many federal officials solicit ideas from dozens of interest groups when they take office, often just to buy time.

Worse, Goffman thought, it could be a trap. One Mr. Gloom scenario went like this: EDF drafts an acid rain plan and publicly backs it. But after bitter internal battles, the administration sends to the Hill a watered-down version that is laughed out of Congress. EDF angers other environmental groups, alienates key Democratic lawmakers and sets back its goal of injecting market incentives into pollution control programs.

Despite his concerns, Goffman huddled in New York between Christmas and New Year's Day with Dr. Daniel Dudek, EDF's chief economist on air issues, James Tripp, the group's general counsel, and Dr. Michael Oppenheimer, its chief atmospheric expert. They pieced together a specific proposal to cap sulfur dioxide (SO_2) emissions from electric power plants and ratchet them down to about half of current levels.

They proposed that the government tell each plant how much pollution to cut, but not how to do it. Instead, companies would be free to pick and choose among all available pollution-control methods. The idea was to give them the flexibility needed to achieve cutbacks at least cost. A company could even meet its obligation by paying for extra cuts to be made at another company's plant, as long as the sum of the two companies' emissions was reduced by the required amount.

Such "emissions trades" could be made freely across state lines, Oppenheimer noted, because acid precipitation is a broad regional problem involving high-altitude mixing of airsheds. Only the Rockies obstruct such mixing, so emissions trading would be divided into just two markets: thirty-one Eastern states, where the bulk of the pollution cuts were required; and seventeen Western states, which would be capped at 1985 levels of SO_2 emissions. Strong local controls would remain in place to protect human health from ground-level SO_2.

The trading scheme largely reflected the work of Dudek. By nature, Dudek was as bold as Goffman was cautious. With a Ph.D. in resource economics from the University of California, Dudek fervently believed that market-oriented incentives could fuel a surge of new progress against air pollution. Nothing else could produce the same gains for so little cost, he insisted. Dudek wrote and preached tirelessly on the subject, prescribing emissions trading schemes to cure every air ill from stratospheric ozone depletion to greenhouse warming. The concept had long appealed to economists on grounds that it would increase efficiency—in other words, save money.

With acid rain, emissions trading would work this way: Say plants X and Y are each ordered to cut SO_2

emissions by five million tons a year. If plant X can do it for $1 a ton, while plant Y has to spend $3 a ton, their aggregate cost would be $20 million.

But if the plants are allowed to trade obligations, they can cut the aggregate cost in half. X could meet both plants' required emission reductions for only $10 million. X could earn profits on its pollution control by charging Y, say, $2 a ton for the SO_2 it controlled on Y's behalf. And for Y, buying pollution control credits from X would be $5 million cheaper than reducing its own SO_2 emissions by the same amount. Everyone gains.

The idea wasn't new. The Environmental Protection Agency had been allowing emissions trading within localities for more than a decade. But far from the clean, efficient machinery envisioned by economists, it was a jury-rigged meshing of gears manipulated by the ingenuity of regulatory lawyers. Still, Dudek believed most of the problems with trading schemes could be solved. What's more, he saw market mechanisms as a sort of magical force that could buffer the clash between demands for environmental quality and economic growth. "Our point," he would say, "is to explore how you can have your cake and eat it too."

As 1989 began, Dudek and Goffman packed up the proposal and started selling it to the incoming administration. Several officials seemed both enthralled with market-oriented solutions and intrigued to find one being advocated by an environmental group.

In February, EPA administrator William Reilly publicly pledged to send Congress major Clean Air Act legislation in a matter of weeks, but the team from EDF couldn't see whether their ideas would play any part in it. Then in March, Boyden Gray called them in.

The visit started inauspiciously. Instead of being swept into the White House, Dudek, Goffman and Krupp were held by the Secret Service outside the White House's southwest gate. It was raining. Gray's office expected them tomorrow, they were told.

Gray invited them in anyway. In his West Wing office, Dudek and Goffman delivered the briefing they had been practicing for weeks. They stressed that the lower cost of their proposal would be consistent with President Bush's no-new-tax pledge, as well as his contention that the country need not choose between a clean environment and economic growth.

As they walked through the details of their trading scheme, Gray started finishing their sentences for them. "Yep, yep, yep, that's absolutely right," he'd say. "This is great, I love it!" Gray displayed intimate knowledge of arcane air pollution regulations. He shared Dudek's faith in markets. His excitement electrified the room.

Gray's ears weren't the only ones inside the administration attuned to EDF's pitch. White House strategists were leaning toward making acid rain the flagship of their Clean Air Act reform, and they saw market incentives as the cheapest way to get strong results.

William Rosenberg, designated to head the EPA's Air and Radiation office, first met Dudek and Goffman carrying his own dog-eared and heavily-annotated copy of *Project 88*.

But as the weather warmed that spring, Rosenberg's

ardor cooled. Dudek had titled his standard briefing, "Acid Rain: An Opportunity for Environmental Perestroika," after Soviet leader Mikhail Gorbachev's program to restructure the inefficient Soviet economy. Like Gorbachev, Rosenberg met resistance from the apparatchiks.

EPA's career bureaucrats favored tight controls affecting only twenty of the most heavily polluting plants. Such a plan, by encouraging installation of stack gas scrubbers, would protect the market for high-sulfur coal and appeal to the United Mine Workers. It also would sharply limit the number of plants whose compliance EPA would have to oversee; by contrast, EDF's proposal would cover more than one hundred plants.

In April, Rosenberg suggested that emissions trading would have only a narrow role in the Bush Clean Air Act proposal. Goffman knew he was on the verge of losing the game.

———

Reaching beyond the administration, EDF staffers worked to soften up opponents and court potential allies.

Some environmental groups, distrusting emissions trading all along, had resented EDF's advocacy for such an approach in *Project 88*. Some saw EDF as out of step, and even called on the group to stop lobbying the new administration.

Goffman and EDF's Tripp sought out David Hawkins and Richard Ayres, veteran attorneys from the Natural Resources Defense Council who were viewed as the world's leading experts on the Clean Air Act. Hawkins had headed the EPA's air programs under President

Jimmy Carter. Ayres led the National Clean Air Coalition, an umbrella group combining a broad range of pollution-control advocates, including EDF. For many, they were the voices of the environmental community on air pollution.

Cautiously, the NRDC lawyers gave Tripp and Goffman a green light to press on with their proposal. But they urged EDF to keep its distance from the new administration.

Dudek and Goffman went on to woo the electric utilities. With Congress poised to impose much stronger medicine to curb acid rain, EDF told utilities that an emissions trading scheme could make the bitter pill more palatable. But they got no more than a polite audience.

EDF then reached for more ammunition from ICF Resources, a Fairfax, Virginia, consulting firm that had built a multi-million-dollar computer model of the nation's utilities. EPA had used it to evaluate the cost and effects of various acid rain proposals. With EPA assistance, Dudek ran EDF's proposal through the model.

The results came back in mid-May, as the administration was beginning to sort out its options. ICF concluded that cranking down emissions with stack gas scrubbers at twenty plants would cost about *$1 billion a year more* than the EDF proposal.

The consultants also backed up Dudek's claim that the trading scheme would help balance the regional impacts of the plan—a political necessity. Regional politics had always been one of the chief barriers to acid rain controls.

Strict, unadorned controls would slap huge costs on

the high-sulfur coal states of the upper Midwest, driving their congressional delegations into ruthless opposition. Most acid rain proposals in recent years had eased this pain with subsidies from states that produce little acid rain. EDF's trading scheme would enlist the free market to accomplish the same goal. ICF predicted, for instance, that expanding Florida utilities would have to purchase credits, and that Ohio utilities would likely sell them. It was still an implicit subsidy, but it allowed Florida lawmakers to avoid voting for an explicit one.

In the next few weeks, EDF found its proposal featured in *The New York Times* and on the CBS morning news. It flooded key administration offices with copies of the ICF study and went on a sales drive.

Dudek and Goffman ambushed Robert Grady, the associate director of the Office of Management and Budget. Goffman worked on Nancy Maloley, a member of the White House Domestic Policy Council staff. Krupp planted a seed in the mind of the President himself. Just before retreating to Camp David to review Clean Air Act options, Bush met with more than a dozen environmental leaders. Krupp, designated to explain the group's consensus on acid rain, threw in EDF's pitch for giving utilities flexibility on how they cut pollution.

The next Monday, June 12, found Dudek, Goffman and Krupp in the large hall in the White House's east wing. They crowded into seats amid scores of politicians and leaders from the various interest groups. All had spent months trying to influence the bill. Most of the decisions now had been made.

In broad strokes, Bush painted the general outlines of his bill. It contained initiatives against acid rain, smog

and toxic air pollutants. The acid rain plan would cut
ten million tons of sulfur dioxide within ten years, and
it sounded like the EDF proposal.

"We've set an ambitious reduction target, and applying market forces will be the fastest, most cost-effective
way to achieve it," Bush said. "So we're allowing utilities to take—to trade credits among themselves for reductions they make, to let them decide how to bring aggregate emissions down as cost-effectively as possible."

Bush said his plan "accounts for continued economic
growth and expansion, offers incentives, choice and
flexibility for industry to find the initiative better than
any previous piece of environmental legislation."

Amidst his explanation, the president threw in his
surprise tribute to EDF and *Project 88* for "bringing
creative solutions to long-standing problems."

For Dudek and Goffman the glow of that accolade
quickly faded. When the EDF pair saw a carefully-
guarded draft of the bill, they found that crucial details
were unacceptable or undecided. While the bill obvi-
ously was meant to reduce SO_2 emissions, one provision
would permit cleaner-running plants to *increase* their
emissions by about one million tons. Worse, the plan
failed to account for the added emissions that would
come from new plants down the road.

"I freaked out," Dudek recalls. He felt that new plants
should be expected to buy emissions credits from existing facilities, producing an automatic offset that would
effectively cap the total amount of SO_2 released. If
new plants weren't required to buy credits, their added

emissions would start to erode the gains won elsewhere; total SO_2 pollution could soar. Moreover, EPA's Air and Radiation office was demanding that utilities file detailed, long-term and binding pollution-control plans that would stifle emissions trading.

On July 10, at the request of OMB's Grady, both Dudek and Goffman worked through the night writing new language for the bill. The next day, Grady's staff took it to an administration drafting session. The rigid utility planning requirements were relaxed. But the loophole for new plants remained wide open.

Dudek and Goffman showered memos on Rosenberg, Gray and other officials in defense of a cap that would take all new sources into account. Without such protection, they argued, the emissions trading market would be hampered, the plan would lose credibility and the initiative would be publicly trashed as a sellout to industry.

Implicit in their protest was a threat. EDF was the only environmental group that had stuck its neck out for any portion of the administration bill. The administration coveted that support. Yet the group was ready to pull back.

In the end, the administration still allowed cleaner plants to increase their emissions, but all new plants were brought in under the cap. White House strategists agreed to this, one official said, only when it became clear that it was the price of EDF's support.

President Bush signed the package July 21 in the White House Rose Garden, calling it "one of the most aggressive pieces of environmental legislation on the Hill." It was greeted by the usual crossfire of special-interest criticism. But both *The Washington Post* and *The New York Times* cited the acid rain section as the strongest part of the bill.

Goffman permitted himself a few minutes of gloating. Amid the old push and pull of interest groups, he said, "Economic efficiency had no constituency in the struggle over acid rain." Now, efficiency achieved through market mechanisms would have an influential constituency: the President.

Of course, Bush's signature ended only the first phase of a new, and perhaps crucial, battle over the Clean Air Act. Lobbyists and congressional committees were sharpening their knives as the document was shipped up Pennsylvania Avenue to Capitol Hill. The utility industry bitterly protested the emissions cap. Environmentalists deplored weaknesses in the controls on toxic chemical emissions and auto pollution.

Initially, Democratic support was scarce, especially in the Senate. But politically, Bush's proposal would be the least a Democratic Congress could approve. The cleanup promised by his acid rain section compared favorably with several congressional bills of recent years. So for acid rain, at least, the bill moved the debate toward tighter controls. With the White House rallying Republicans behind it, Bush appeared to be laying a bipartisan foundation for fairly strong acid rain legislation using market incentives.

EDF found itself in a delicate balancing act. Goffman praised the bill's acid rain section, while pointing out that EDF still favored strengthening that and other sections of the measure. Key Democratic lawmakers complained that EDF was softpedalling its criticisms. The

White House protested that it was being too critical. A friend of Goffman's from another environmental group ribbed him, "How does it feel to be riding the tiger?"

It was a rough ride, but Goffman believed it would be worth the bruises. "It is a lot more demanding and risky to get involved in proposing things," Goffman said. "But the potential gains are huge."

Others dismissed the words as empty rhetoric. But EDF's Tom Graff and Zach Willey took them as an invitation.

Graff, a politically canny lawyer who had founded EDF's California office, spotted them deep in a 200-page, 1975 electric rate-hike decision by the California Public Utilities Commission. "The most important task facing utilities" was conservation, the commission declared. It deplored "unchecked proliferation of power plants," prescribed alternative power supplies as well as energy efficiency, and pledged to adjust rates depending on the "vigor, imagination and effectiveness" with which utilities applied the prescription.

At the time, the words sounded mildly revolutionary. California electric utilities were on a building binge. Environmentalists were fighting planned coal and nuclear plant construction. Both sides were girding for battle over an anti-nuclear initiative on the 1976 state ballot. The words in the PUC decision had been penned by Leonard Ross, the first appointee named to the commission by Governor Jerry Brown, whose own visionary rhetoric led to his caricature as "Governor Moonbeam." And, at first, the words seemed to have about a moonbeam's impact.

But Graff and Willey decided to call the commission's bluff. Why not take Ross's language at face value? A review of recent research convinced Willey that conservation and alternative power sources—such as geothermal and cogeneration—not only caused less environmental harm than coal or nuclear plants, *but also might be cheaper*.

Willey was probably the first Ph.D. economist to take a long-term job with any environmental group. Six-foot-four and lean as a fence rail, he was a contrarian with doubts about the benefits of high-tech solutions. As an economic consultant in the Middle East, he had worried that mechanized farming would exacerbate class differences. Visiting Egypt, he had noted farmland decline stemming from the Aswan dam.

From scouring the economic journals, Willey had begun to suspect that electric utilities were investing too heavily in large power plants. Their earnings were based on a percentage of their investments in such things, so why wouldn't they?

With a young man's disregard for authority, he calmly set out to set straight the utilities' planning departments. He aimed to prove that alternatives to big coal and nuclear plants would benefit not only the environment but utility ratepayers and stockholders as well. Before he finished, Willey was to design a whole new way of looking at electric power companies—one in which conservation investments could generate the same profits as new plants.

It was a powerful vision that, etched into a computer model of EDF's design, claimed to point the way to a better future. In fact, it would ultimately induce California utilities to steer a U-turn in the ensuing decade away from their historic focus on massive new power plants. The change, of course, would prove a timely one; it helped them avoid the financial disasters of half-built plants that plagued the Washington Public Power Supply

System (WPPSS, sometimes pronounced "whoops") and several other utilities as costs rose and demand fell.

But in the 1970's no one seemed to know what to make of Willey. He talked of economic incentives and profits, not trees or snail darters. His demonstrations occurred not in the streets or courts, but in regulatory hearings, balance sheets and a computer model that few could fathom.

One of Willey's achievements was to show that environmentalists could out-plan the utility planners. As EDF attorney David Roe was to say years later, "We play the game on their turf, by their rules. It's a complicated game, but once you learn it, it's like riding a bicycle."

———

Willey took a practice swing at the issue in a paper he wrote in 1976 for the Federal Reserve Bank of San Francisco. Asked to write on the nuclear power debate, he looked into whether energy conservation could render costly nuclear plants unnecessary. His answer was yes.

Willey relied heavily on projections by the Lawrence Berkeley Laboratory, a federally-assisted institution near his Berkeley office that had done millions of dollars of energy research since the first Arab oil embargo. At the time, California's utilities were saying they would need about $20 billion over the next ten years to build new plants. Lawrence Berkeley Laboratory estimated only about $3.5 billion. The $16.5 billion difference stemmed from the Berkeley lab's assumption that consumers would use electricity more efficiently. With such huge savings in capital costs achievable, Willey reasoned, it would be worth spending large sums to encourage conservation.

From 1976 through 1978, with the Public Utilities Commission hearings as his forum, Willey worked to show that an alternative development path would pay off for Pacific Gas & Electric Co., the nation's largest investor-owned utility.

Graduating from a hand calculator to a computer, Willey pieced together a mathematical model of the huge utility's finances. With help from EDF's Daniel Kirshner, a self-taught computer modeler, he laid out the system's workings on a detailed level that no one outside the company had ever attempted. He worked out how PG&E would perform under its own plan to build ten new power plants in twenty years, right down to consumer rates and earnings per share.

Then he built alternatives. He selected building blocks from a range of "soft" energy options—from wind farms to cogeneration, the production of electricity from industry's surplus heat. He filled in hard numbers generated by Lawrence Berkeley Laboratory and others on each option's cost and potential power production.

Hurdling beyond the conventional options, he added conservation *as an additional energy source*. Like generation, conservation produces spare energy that can be sold, he reasoned, so why not treat the two alike? Consciously taking the next step into heresy, Willey provided for conservation to be financed just like power plants. A utility could buy home insulation or more efficient appliances for its customers, he suggested, then add the expense to the rate base on which it earned an approved rate of return.

Alternative Energy Sources

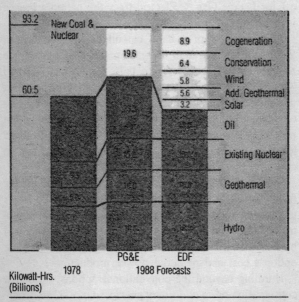

93.2	New Coal & Nuclear	
	19.6	
	8.9	Cogeneration
	6.4	Conservation
	5.8	Wind
	5.6	Add. Geothermal
	3.2	Solar
60.5		Oil
		Existing Nuclear
		Geothermal
		Hydro

PG&E   EDF

Kilowatt-Hrs.   1978   1988 Forecasts
(Billions)

New energy options would eliminate the need for new coal and nuclear plants and reduce the demand for oil to generate electricity, according to a 10-year forecast submitted by EDF in 1978. The new options would handle the same growth in demand as PG&E's conventional plan.

The beauty of it, from Willey's perspective, was that everybody gained. Electric rates could be held down. The risk of building huge, and hugely expensive, new plants could be avoided. And utility profits could actually rise by $75 million per year.

By the time it was completed in 1978, Willey's alternative scenario of PG&E's future filled a 125-page document, densely packed with numbers that backed up the computer calculations. It was unveiled with pride—to almost complete public indifference.

A press conference called to announce the report flopped. When Willey testified before the California PUC, PG&E's attorney made only a perfunctory effort to question the analysis. "How can I cross-examine a bunch of footnotes?" he complained.

The job of selling Willey's work fell to David Roe, a young lawyer who had joined EDF's California office in 1976 and had soon taken over the power company project from Graff. A former Rhodes scholar whose great-grandfather had founded PG&E, Roe regarded the company as so blinded by inertia that it couldn't see its own self-interest. Willey had "built a better mousetrap," in Roe's view, but the world didn't beat a path to his door. So Roe, Willey and Kirshner set out to pave the way.

Roe planned to seek a financial penalty against PG&E for failing to pursue conservation and alternatives. EDF had tried the same thing in 1976, armed with a less sophisticated analysis by Willey, to no avail. But, by 1978, Roe felt he was making progress. The PUC staff, critical of PG&E's conservation and alternative power efforts, had recommended a slight cut in the rate of return, which helped make the concept of a rate penalty thinkable. But the commission and its staff were known for caution and deliberation. And when EDF looked around for allies, none was to be found.

Sylvia Siegel, the feisty consumer-advocate gadfly of the California PUC, objected bitterly to letting utilities charge ratepayers for their conservation investments. "That's a stupid goddam idea," declared Mrs. Siegel, executive director of Towards Utility Rate Normalization, a San Francisco-based group. Calling the proposal another boondoggle for utility shareholders, she charged that EDF staffers "are showing an absolute disregard for the inequities and impacts on ratepayers."

Other environmental groups weren't much happier. While they liked the bottom line—no big new power plants—most hated the idea of letting a utility invest in alternative energy plants or conservation. "Small is beautiful" was in fashion in the counter-culture. "Soft" energy guru Amory Lovins was calling big utilities obsolete, and predicting their replacement by small independent power producers.

The prevailing view among soft-energy advocates, Roe recalls, was: "The only way to get where we want to go is to grind the utilities to dust and have somebody else make the power."

Roe felt isolated, exposed. Environmentalists were supposed to fight business, the convention went, and now, "It looked to our colleagues like we were siding with industry."

Pacific Gas & Electric Co., of course, saw EDF as a

threat. Willey's suggestions, it said, "are presumptuous, arrogant and should be rejected outright."

_____

The contest quickly extended beyond the PUC. In 1978, 30-second ads had started airing across northern California. One, showing a six-year-old boy telling another about "driving my sun car up to my sun house," gently disparaged people who "think the sun can do anything." Another featured a four-year-old girl putting a toy refrigerator and washing machine into a dollhouse. A voice said, "We'll need a lot more electricity . . . even with conservation . . . so we need government approvals to start building now."

"Look at this. It's outrageous!" Roe yelled to his colleagues when a bootlegged copy of the script arrived in his mail. Roe knew EDF couldn't afford competing air time. He was still mumbling about it hours later when Kirshner suggested: "Isn't there an equal-time rule or something for television ads?"

It took months of haggling, but EDF lined up more than thirty stations willing to air a free rebuttal. The next spring, the response beamed out to much of the state. One EDF ad featured an actor who announced that the local power company had discovered "a brand new source of energy." He then lit a dollar bill and held it, burning, while he talked of cheaper alternatives to the increasing cost of coal, oil and uranium. "But your utility doesn't care," he said at the end. "It thinks you have money to burn."

Filming took 37 takes, the producer said. "We had

a hell of a time getting the money to burn right, and after a while the actor started flubbing his lines. We started with a twenty, but after two takes, we realized we'd better switch to ones."

PG&E had begun urging consumers to conserve power and use efficient appliances, but had done almost nothing directly. In a series of PUC hearings, Roe showed that California utilities had given little more than lip service to conservation and alternative power projects.

As time went on, Roe and Willey picked up some key supporters. Leo McCarthy, the influential Speaker of the California Assembly, endorsed letting utilities add the cost of solar and conservation devices to their rate-bases. With McCarthy's support, the governor's office also came out for utility investment in conservation and solar power.

By late 1979, after almost three years of regulatory wrangling, the wall around PG&E began to crumble.

The first stone fell after Roe proved that PG&E had given short shrift to cogeneration partnerships with industry. PG&E had identified enough promising cogeneration prospects to replace three nuclear power plants. But in four years, Roe showed, the utility had talked to only eight of forty-six potential cogenerators.

Company lawyers went to the top brass, warning that they risked being hit with a rate penalty, according to Roe's book, *Dynamos and Virgins*. "Look," one reportedly said, "our legal position is really weak, and the company is going to look very bad unless we do something about it right now."

PG&E announced it would pay cogenerators as much for their power as the company itself would have had to spend to make it—by building a new plant, for instance.

The concession was crucial. PG&E had haggled with cogenerators for as long as nine years, refusing to buy their excess energy for even a fraction of what it was spending for its own power. In Roe's words, the decision opened the door "for anyone to make electricity with decentralized technology—a windmill, for example—and be sure of getting a market price for it, from the company that used to be able to freeze out all electricity but its own."

The move failed to mollify the PUC. Soon a bigger stone fell. The commission ruled that PG&E had inexcusably dragged its feet on cogeneration. It imposed a penalty of $7.2 million a year for two years, or until the utility put 600 new megawatts of cogenerated power into service. Though the amount was dwarfed by the utility's newest rate hike, the penalty was "incredibly significant" at the time, recalls Willey. "It told PG&E that they had to think about alternatives, and that cost-minimization matters."

In March 1980, less than three months later, the power company established the nation's largest program to help building owners finance conservation. This "Zero Interest Program" gave customers interest-free loans for such things as insulation, storm windows and low-flow showerheads. Funding soon soared to $100 million. *The Los Angeles Times* compared it to the discovery of gold at Sutter's Mill. PG&E also established a new, long-range planning department, which soon began canceling future power plant projects.

The lesson wasn't lost on Southern California Edison, the state's second-largest electric utility. In the fall of 1980, Edison announced plans to develop nearly 2000 megawatts of power from alternative sources, the equivalent of two large power plants.

As the 1980's dawned, one major power project resisted the new economics, and it had environmental groups steaming. Both leading California utilities planned to invest in a huge coal mine and power complex in southwestern Utah. The Allen-Warner Valley plant was slated to generate 2500 megawatts, the equivalent of two-and-a-half large nuclear plants. The coal mine would spew dust and noise into the air near Bryce Canyon National Park. Crushed coal would be mixed with precious Western water and pumped through a long "slurry" pipeline to a complex of coal-fired boilers and electric turbines.

Environmental groups saw the project as a dire threat to clear air and clean water throughout the region. But, once again, EDF would make a case before the California PUC based solely on economics. Kirshner ran the plant and alternatives through the EDF utility model, and the alternatives came back about $500 million cheaper.

Though the project was backed by the Carter administration, a tide of opinion turned against it. *The New York Times*, praising EDF's contribution, wrote that, "Inertia and lack of imagination, not cost advantage, now drive utilities toward conventional solutions to energy needs."

Staffers for the California Energy Commission also took EDF's side, urging the project be dropped. While

Global Energy Efficiency

U.S. energy use efficiency (of which electrical energy is just a part) has improved over the past decade, though it is still worse than that of most other countries. Shown is energy consumption in tons of oil equivalent per $1000 of gross domestic product.

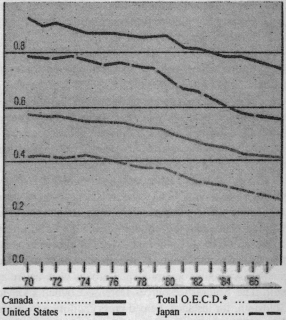

| Canada .... ▬▬ | Total O.E.C.D.* ... ▬ ▬ |
| United States .... ▬▬ ▬▬ | Japan .... ▬▬ ▬▬ |

* Organization for Economic Cooperation and Development

Source: Cambridge Energy Research Associates

the energy commission had no direct authority, its recommendation could be influential. So just before it took final action, the two giant power companies abruptly withdrew their application for approval of the Allen-Warner Valley project.

"Here was victory of more than words or dollars," David Roe wrote later. "There was still nothing official, even now no formal verdict in our favor, but here indisputably was a $5 billion brontosaurus, dead at our feet. Zach Willey's idea had killed it."

In the decade since Willey unveiled his model, California utilities have not had to break ground for even a single large power plant. PG&E says 8% of its power now comes from cogeneration and about 2% from hydroelectric, solar, wind and other renewable energy sources. Alternative supplies have left the state with spare capacity for at least the next eight years. And PG&E has invested more than $1 billion in conservation.

Perhaps it could have happened without Willey, Kirshner, Roe and EDF. The spike in interest rates in the late 1970's helped discourage capital-intensive building plans, and the simultaneous surge in oil prices depressed demand. California Governor Brown brought new people into state government who welcomed change. And other environmental groups were active as well. The Natural Resources Defense Council's David Goldstein, for instance, helped press California to establish appliance energy efficiency standards that promise major conservation gains.

Promotion of conservation developed simultaneously in the Northeast and Pacific Northwest. But, outside

California, alternative power sources haven't been widely tapped.

In California, Willey's vision has become conventional wisdom. Today, the state PUC uses the EDF model to assess growth options. Alternative power providers lease it to calculate the rates they should earn. And to Roe's "great satisfaction," PG&E itself now leases the model from EDF for about $25,000 a year.

In much of the western U.S., precious water is to cities and farmers what Jerusalem is to Arabs and Jews: an object of unrelenting struggle.

Consider the response of a Denver Water Board member to a study showing that water conservation would be cheaper than building a new dam. "Listen, you people," he said, by one account. "If you think we're going to save water so that some son of a bitch in Tucson can fill his swimming pool, you've got another think coming."

In California, irrigation district officials sputtered with anger when EDF's Zach Willey began to suggest that they sell excess water to the cities for premium prices. At one meeting, Willey recalls, "I think I almost came to fisticuffs; there was a guy from Kern County that was jumping up and down."

Yet EDF has demonstrated that both of these controversial options to stretch water supplies—conservation and water transfers—make good economic sense. In 1989, the group had a role in water wars at both ends of the Colorado River. One led to a precedent-setting solution; another to a head-on collision.

In 1977, when California Governor Jerry Brown cut a deal to settle one of the state's perennial water fights, EDF's Tom Graff and Zach Willey weren't buying.

Brown said he would support building the Peripheral Canal, a giant tap designed to drain the tributaries of

San Francisco Bay for thirsty Southern California. In return, southern water districts agreed to guarantee that they would leave untouched the remaining wild Northern California rivers and limit any drainage from tributaries that supported the wetlands, fish and shellfish of the Bay's estuary.

The problem, complained Willey, was that the canal was to be built with lots of spare capacity. Sooner or later, he reasoned, the guarantees would be washed away by demands to fill the canal with more water. "It was concrete versus paper," he said.

The governor and the canal's supporters managed to push the compact through the state legislature, but still needed voter approval in a 1982 referendum. Graff and EDF opposed it, joining an odd opposition alliance that included conservationists, conservatives and wealthy corporate farmers. They called the project too big and too costly. Enough voters agreed to send the plan down to defeat.

During the referendum campaign, Graff had argued that there were cheaper and less damaging sources of water for Southern California. Several broad studies had hailed the potential benefits of water marketing. Graff wanted to prove it in a specific case. "There was lots of macro rhetoric," recalls Willey. "What was needed was a micro demonstration."

So Graff and Willey hired economics graduate student Robert Stavins (who later became a Harvard assistant professor and editor of *Project 88*) to study the economic feasibility of one long-discussed possibility.

The projected trade would involve the Metropolitan Water District of Southern California ("Met"), serving

homes and industry from San Diego to Ventura, and
the Imperial Irrigation District, serving an agricultural
region 150 miles southeast of Los Angeles. Stavins as-
sessed what it would cost Met to finance the prevention
of water loss in Imperial's system—by lining leaky canals and reusing irrigation water, for instance. He figured Met's payoff would be to get access to the saved
water (or equal volumes of water diverted upstream) for
sale to its urban customers.

As an economist, Willey had long fretted over irrigators' failure to conserve water. Agriculture got almost
90% of Southern California's Colorado River water, and
used it freely. Water loss was notorious at Imperial,
where it flowed into the brackish Salton Sea or seeped
into briny groundwater, from which it couldn't be recovered. The state had even ordered Imperial to develop
conservation plans after one farmer, his fields flooded
by the rising Salton Sea, protested that he was losing
land due to Imperial's waste.

One problem was that irrigators enjoyed federally-
subsidized water prices. Their water was so cheap that
they had little incentive to conserve it. Only if the price
rose would these farmers become interested in major
conservation measures. And a good way to encourage
that would be to let them sell water to willing urban
buyers at market rates. "I knew you were going to have
to give the farmers some compensation for their water,"
Willey says. "That led to water marketing, which would
provide them with a substantial carrot—as well as give
them incentives to reconsider how they irrigate and what
they irrigate."

Willey argued that farmers would phase out inefficient

water uses such as cotton farming and cow pasture irrigation—the agricultural equivalent of "gas guzzler" au-
tos—if they could profit more by selling the water to
the cities.

For Willey, water exchanges carried forward the same
concept that he had advanced in the electric power field.
Exploiting the right economic incentives allowed all
sides to benefit. It was a win-win situation.

In March 1983, Stavins's report documented Willey's
view. It contended that, in the Imperial Irrigation District
alone, more than 400,000 acre-feet of water per year
could be saved for Met's use at a cost of $821 per
acre-foot. (One acre-foot, about 326,000 gallons, would
cover an acre of land one foot deep in water.) The two
major alternatives that would tap Northern California
water would each cost $100 to $300 *more* per acre-
foot, he said. The potential savings were huge. Even a
medium-sized conservation program, Stavins estimated,
could save Met $95 million a year.

For two years, Graff and Willey touted the Met-Impe-
rial water exchange in a flurry of papers, articles and
interviews. The idea was controversial. Some farmers
feared loss of their water rights. Others worried that
once a much higher value was placed on their water,
they could forget about getting any more federal subsidies for water projects. Some citizen groups protested
against letting farmers profit by reselling water that the
federal government's Bureau of Reclamation gave them
at a taxpayer-subsidized price.

Met and Imperial officials responded cautiously. Carl
Boronkay, Met's legal counsel at the time, initially
warned that "a host of laws" could block a deal. But

Conserved Irrigation Water Will Flow to Metropolitan District

within a year, Boronkay was declaring that "adequate authority now exists" for the compact.

Negotiations started in 1985, and ran for four years before the parties sealed the first major demonstration of water marketing in California. Boronkay, coauthoring a description of the deal in EDF's newsletter, wrote that it should "serve as a model to assist other, possibly disparate water agencies in reaching similar accords."

The deal "certainly provides a model that we all talk about and want to use," agreed Robert Potter, deputy director of the state Department of Water Resources. Potter credited EDF with having provided the first detailed economic justification he had seen for a specific water exchange; the group played "a very important and sometimes creative role," he said, in getting Met and Imperial together.

Today, Willey is working on water marketing projects in several Western states.

One goal is to round up enough water-sellers to replace 70,000 acre-feet that Los Angeles drains annually from remote Mono Lake, a rate that threatens to reduce the nation's oldest lake to a puddle.

Willey has also started advising Native American tribes on how to get better use of their water without damming more rivers. Across the West, Native Americans are pressing more than fifty separate water rights claims, a situation that could lead to a new regional surge in dam building.

Willey is again playing broker and adviser, not adversary: "If you go after people to take things away from them, they're going to resist. But if you can give them a benefit, then they can come along on their own terms and the environment stands to benefit sooner."

In Colorado, EDF's Dan Luecke found even more stubborn resistance from the powerful Denver Water Department. To stop the Department's planned Two Forks Dam, he had to help convince EPA to block it.

In 1980, EDF had sponsored a study of Denver area water use by Colorado University economist John Morris. The study concluded that the city could reap big water savings by taking relatively simple steps to encourage conservation.

Morris found that many Denver customers didn't even have water meters; they paid the same amount regardless of their use. More efficient water use could also be achieved with improved toilets, shower heads, landscaping practices and industrial uses, he found. The potential savings totalled more than 50,000 acre-feet per year, about half the amount to be provided by the planned Two Forks Dam.

A dam at Two Forks would inundate fourteen miles of the best trout waters in the country, creating reservoirs on both forks of the South Platte River and harming whooping crane habitat downstream in Nebraska. Twice before in the twentieth century a dam on the narrow canyon had been proposed and blocked. Yet the Denver Water Department wouldn't look at any major alternative.

At the time of Morris's report, Luecke was moving to EDF's Denver office from Boston, where he had taught at Harvard and worked as a consulting engineer. Morris's report had been endorsed by Denver's *Rocky Mountain News*. Luecke thought, "Who could argue with this?" His answer came from the Denver Water Department, which publicly denounced it. "I realized then that this was a different kind of ball game," Luecke says.

That the department saw no need to compromise should have come as no surprise. Its power in the region was enormous, and politically, it was on a roll.

At the time, Ronald Reagan was taking over the federal government and filling prominent jobs with right-wing allies of Denver brewing magnate Joseph Coors. It was clear that environmental criticism of dam projects wouldn't get much support from Washington.

Still, Luecke and Robert Golten of the National Wildlife Federation tried to press for alternatives within a new forum called the Denver Metropolitan Water Roundtable. The roundtable included Colorado politicians from both sides of the continental divide, several water district officials, area businessmen, and the two environmentalists.

Within the roundtable, Luecke and Golten represented all the leading Colorado environmental groups. Chaired initially by Bob Weaver, executive director of the state's Trout Unlimited, this "environmental caucus" got together regularly to make decisions and plan strategy.

The caucus offered to design alternatives to Two Forks Dam, but the water department refused to give them access to its model of the huge system of reservoirs and canals.

Ultimately, Luecke built his own model. He hired hydrology engineer Lee Rozaklis to compile mountains of data going back to 1947 on stream flows, reservoir levels, water exchanges, distribution patterns and use. Luecke borrowed a computer terminal that could tap into the mainframe at the nearby National Center for

Atmospheric Research, and he and Rozaklis fed the data into his model.

"I thought quite literally I was going to go blind sitting in front of that terminal 18 hours a day, seven days a week," Luecke recalls. But he got the analysis done.

The environmental caucus's strategy was to collect a little water here, a little there. It backed a new dam to enlarge an existing reservoir on the North Fork; it suggested improvements on other existing dams, better integration with other water systems and, of course, conservation. The combined plan would produce 20% more water than Two Forks, according to the caucus, at half the cost. The proposal promised to satisfy even the water department's own estimates of need through 2010, though Luecke claimed that the underlying population projections were inflated.

But the water department and its allies brushed the proposal aside, contending that a Two Forks dam was crucial to the growth of forty-one suburban communities. It hired the U.S. Army Corps of Engineers to conduct an environmental impact statement (EIS), the prerequisite for construction.

The Corps was known for seldom seeing a dam it didn't like. It made no exception at Two Forks. It accumulated a smorgasbord of ideas on how to mitigate the environmental effect of the dam and then endorsed permitting construction.

The finding outraged Dennis Sohocki, who headed EPA's review of the permit. In memos to Regional Administrator James Scherer, he argued that the EIS was biased. The corps had rejected water conservation out of hand, he said, and ignored alternative dams and improvements that would be less damaging to the environment. He called Cheesman Canyon, which would be drowned by the dam, "an irreplaceable resource with one of the most productive and highly used trout streams in Colorado." Sohocki recommended that EPA block the permit.

Still, Scherer was expected to approve the dam. So environmentalists protested privately to EPA administrator William Reilly. Leaders of eleven national environmental groups signed a letter calling Two Forks, "simply the most destructive way of supplying water to the Denver metropolitan area."

Their letters charged that Denver's water department had welshed on commitments it made in the late 1970's. In return for acquiescence from environmentalists for a dam and the Foothills Water Treatment Plant, the water board had agreed to save up to 80,000 acre-feet of water annually with a major conservation program throughout the Denver service area. If that had been done, Denver would need only another 18,000 acre-feet to meet its 2010 needs, the environmental groups said.

Colorado's Democratic Senator Tim Wirth, who brokered the Foothills compromise, echoed the environmentalists' concerns. Lame-duck Republican Senator Bill Armstrong weighed in against them, warning that without Two Forks, Denver suburbs would buy enough irrigation water to dry out as much as 100,000 acres of farmland. Governor Roy Romer had opposed building Two Forks, but urged EPA not to stand in its way.

In March 1989, after a meeting with Luecke, EDF executive director Fred Krupp, and leaders from American Rivers, the National Audubon Society and the National Wildlife Federation, EPA's Reilly stepped into the fray. He announced a formal review of the permit, blocking the dam on grounds that there were less damaging alternatives. He reaffirmed the decision that August.

Reilly's decision sparked mixed reactions in the region. The *Rocky Mountain News* fired an angry dissent, but the *Denver Post* commentary was philosophical, and praise came from the Boulder *Daily Camera*. A poll of Denver residents found 47% opposed and only 32% favoring the dam.

Outside Colorado, the action drew strong praise to the young Bush administration. Some took it as the first proof that Bush was to be an environmentalist in more than rhetoric.

After Reilly's announcement, Luecke visited the governor's and mayor's offices, saying he and other environmentalists were prepared to work on new substitutes for Two Forks. But again, the proffered carrot was rejected.

Luecke awaits the next step. "I hope we can start looking at options other than litigation," he said recently. But if the water department sues to obtain a permit, he said, "we'll intervene in defense of EPA."

EPILOGUE

Unlike the greenhouse effect or the stratospheric ozone hole, the environmental problems of EDF's early years were comparatively down-to-earth. Founding chairman Dennis Puleston, as he studied DDT's effects on wildlife nearly a quarter century ago, would climb straight up to osprey nests and count the damaged eggs from which young birds would never hatch. The small drama was being played out in his own backyard.

Who could have guessed that this drama would become the landmark case that started modern environmental law? Who could have known it would launch a group whose work would plumb the depths of the sea and reach into the upper atmosphere? EDF's founders, in fact, might never have banded together and gone to court, had only the Suffolk County Mosquito Control Commission politely heard their concerns about the osprey.

"But they refused to listen to us," Puleston recalls. "They said that DDT was killing mosquitoes, and that was their job, and it was cheap and easy to apply, and they were not concerned with any other organisms that were being affected by DDT. And then we realized that the only way to stop them was to file a court action."

Given their day in court, EDF's founders were quick to show the global scope of their backyard drama. They testified that DDT was moving up the food chain, spreading as far as Antarctica, taking a heavy toll on wildlife, even contaminating mother's milk. It was by revealing DDT's remote and unwanted consequences— *and* safer alternatives—that EDF helped end its use.

"Even at the very start, we were coming in with alternatives," Puleston says, recalling recommendations of integrated pest management and less-persistent pesticides such as methoxychlor. The group's emphasis on solutions "helped keep EDF from being perceived as the Abominable No Man."

After winning the injunction that stopped the spraying of DDT in Suffolk County, Puleston and his colleagues pursued the pesticide from state to state for nearly five years. Their efforts ultimately convinced the fledgling Environmental Protection Agency to ban the sale of DDT nationwide in 1972. EPA's action, at long last, answered the eloquent plea that Rachel Carson had voiced on behalf of wildlife in *Silent Spring*. Ten years earlier, her plea had fallen on deaf ears at the Department of Agriculture. But times had changed, and the invention of environmental law had helped change them.

Invention is a way of life at EDF, as the stories in this book have shown. What most characterizes the group's achievements is not that they are legal or scientific or economic or diplomatic, but that they are *unconventional*. Innovative thinking is the mainstay that has kept EDF ahead of the curve and made the group a potent force for change.

The natural world will benefit as more inventive thinking arises from all quarters. "It's time to put our best minds to work," President Bush said in announcing his Clean Air Act proposal, "to turn technology and the power of the marketplace to the advantage of the environment—to create, to innovate, to tip the scales in favor of recovery, restoration and renewal."

———————

Dennis Puleston, who has just turned 84 and who recently returned from his 32nd voyage to Antarctica, still climbs up to the osprey nests to count eggs near his Long Island home. But now the eggs are hatching, and the ospreys—once on the verge of disappearing as a breeding bird—have returned in force. Although toxic byproducts of DDT persisted in the environment for many years, they have now declined to the point where "things are very much on the upswing for the ospreys," according to Puleston, "and there is every reason to believe they will recover fully."

After seeing the number of osprey chicks on Long Island plummet to about a dozen in the mid-1960's, he is delighted to report that more than two hundred fledglings hatched this year. "If nature is given half a chance," he says, "it is remarkable how she will recover after all the abuses she receives from man. She has wonderful powers of recovery, which is surely a hopeful note."

ABOUT THE AUTHOR

Robert E. Taylor, who prepared this book with assistance from the EDF staff, is a veteran journalist who covered politics and government in Washington for fifteen years. He has written for *The Boston Globe*, *The Providence Journal*, *The Philadelphia Bulletin*, and *The Wall Street Journal*. At *The Wall Street Journal*, he covered issues ranging from banking to the law, and focused on environmental and energy reporting from 1985-87. Taylor now reports on the environment for the *Seattle Post-Intelligencer*.

ENVIRONMENTAL DEFENSE FUND OFFICES

National Headquarters
257 Park Avenue South
New York, NY 10010
212 505-2100

1616 P Street, N.W.
Washington, DC 20036
202 387-3500

5655 College Avenue
Oakland, CA 94618
415 658-8008

1405 Arapahoe Avenue
Boulder, CO 80302
303 440-4901

1108 East Main Street
Richmond, VA 23219
804 780-1297

128 East Hargett Street
Raleigh, NC 27605
919 821-7793

1800 Guadalupe
Austin, TX 78701
512 478-5161